BETWEEN KNOWING AND BELIEVING

PIERRE LECOMTE DU NOÜY

BETWEEN KNOWING
AND BELIEVING

ILLUSTRATIONS BY BAZAINE

Translated from the French by
Mary Lecomte du Noüy

Introduction by George N. Shuster,
Assistant to the President, University of Notre Dame
President Emeritus, Hunter College

With a Foreword by Albert Delaunay
of the Pasteur Institute, Paris

DAVID MCKAY COMPANY, INC.
NEW YORK

First edition in French
ENTRE SAVOIR ET CROIRE
Hermann, Paris, 1964.
First American Edition, 1966
Printed in France

Q 171
L 413
1967

JAN 15 1988

CONTENTS

BIOGRAPHICAL NOTES

1883

December 20th: Pierre Lecomte du Noüy was born in Paris, 6 place de Rennes.

1896-1902

Lecomte du Noüy's education was seriously interrupted by ill health while at both the Lycée du Havre and the Lycée Carnot in Paris. During a cruise to Sicily he was able to have enlightening talks wilh the Poincaré brothers.

1904

The determined efforts he made to improve his health by developing his muscles in the open air enabled him to catch up with his studies. He simultaneously entered the Faculties of Law, of Political Science, and of Oriental Languages. During his military service he was promoted to the rank of lieutenant.

1907-1912

After obtaining his degree in Political Science and Oriental Languages, Lecomte du Noüy was appointed secretary to Aristide Briand, who was then Minister of Justice. During these years he published numerous articles and short stories and wrote successful plays, one of which was produced by the celebrated director, Antoine of the Odéon. The summer of 1909 was spent with Maurice Maeterlinck at the Abbaye de St Wandrille, where he acted in *Macbeth* directed by Georgette Leblanc. He then acted with great success in a play by Francis de Croisset. In 1910 he obtained his degree of Doctor of Law, but neither law nor his easy successes on the stage interested him as much as philosophy. Convinced that modern philosophy must rest on science, he decided to take courses in physics and chemistry at the Sorbonne and worked under Appell, Curie, and Lippman.

1914-16

Mobilized at the outbreak of war, Lecomte du Noüy was transferred in 1915 to the Field Hospital directed by Dr. Carrel. His experiments enabled him to establish the curve of cicatrization of wounds. Publication of his first scientific paper.

1917

He obtained his degree of Doctor of Science at the University of Paris with his thesis on *The Cicatrization of Wounds*.

1920.

Attached to the Rockefeller Institute of New York, where he had already been sent on missions in 1917 and 1919, he remained there until 1927. He installed the first physicochemical laboratory entirely devoted to biological problems, thus creating biophysics. Manufacture of his Tensiometer.

1921-27

Experiments on Energy and Vision: *Measurements of the Surface Tension of Serum; Adsorption; Monomolecular Layers; Measurements of the three dimen-*

sions of the Molecule of Sodium Oleate; New Method for determining the value of the Constant N of Avogadro. His experiments on Surface Tension were assembled in his book: Surface Equilibria of Colloid Solutions. Invention of a new Viscosimeter.

1927-36

Appointed head of a department at the Pasteur Institute in Paris, he created with little financial aid and only a few assistants a modern laboratory which became a model visited by scientists from all over the world. Studies on *The Critical Temperature of Serum (55° C)*. Experiments in: *Viscosity, Rotatory Power, Rotatory Dispersion, Optic Density, Adsorption, Diffused Light, Factor of Depolarization, Ionic Equilibria, Electric Conductivity, the pH, Absorption in the Ultraviolet, Spectrophotometry in the Visible and in the Infrared*. Invention of numerous instruments for his experiments. Discovery of 12 unknown phenomena.

1935

Publication of *Biological Time* and *The Critical Temperature of Serum*, containing the results of his experiments on immunized and non-immunized blood serum. After his resignation from the Pasteur Institute he was named a director of the Ecole des Hautes Etudes with a laboratory at the Sorbonne.
Though Lecomte du Noüy was an agnostic at the beginning of his life, he had gradually become convinced that science did not imply materialism. About this time, he developed a faith which was neither specific nor Christian but simply implied the existence of Spirit and of a creation willed by a Creator.

1942.

Publication of *L'Avenir de l'Esprit* (Paris, Gallimard) awarded the Prix Vitet by the French Academy. Escape from Paris

1944-1946

Publication of *La Dignité Humaine* (New York, Brentano). Lectures on France in 34 states of the US, in Army, Aviation, and Navy camps. Pamphlet *Is God out of Date?* written for the Y.M.C.A. Writing of *Human Destiny*.

1947

Publication of *Human Destiny*. Hospitalized in New York in July, Lecomte du Noüy died on September 22nd without knowing the worldwide success of his book.

INTRODUCTION

The essays which follow this brief introduction are of absorbing interest in their own right, but they have sovereign importance because they reflect Lecomte du Noüy's progress toward the goal he reached in Human Destiny. *That admirable book, far more widely and steadily read than any other of its kind since it first appeared in 1947, was not just another attempt to reconcile science and religion. This the two moving letters of Teilhard de Chardin, which have been added to the present American edition of the essays, make very clear. Both great French scientists, each in his own incomparable way, sought to set free once again the " powers of love, " so that they might restore meaning to human birth, growth, and death. One complements and indeed completes the other. The fact is all the more remarkable because, unlike Chardin the Jesuit, du Noüy had been reared a skeptic for whom religion lay outside the intellectual concerns of a modern man.*

When Human Destiny *appeared it was one of a number of books in which biologists of the time dissented from the then widely held view that their science disavowed any difference between man and beast or proved that Divinity shapes no one's ends. They asked: has not the scientist, in his search for clues to the mystery of Evolution, been so intent on finding traces of the transformation of ape into man that he has risked giving the impression that he has forgotten what man truly is or at least could be? And, of course, as one looked at what was happening in the world — at the inexorable logic which led from concentration camp to gas chamber — it was hardly possible to avoid the conclusion that men, who had been told they were only beasts of somewhat unusual shape and coloration, might have decided to be what they were supposed to be. The doctrine that only the fittest survive, grossly and erroneously interpreted, led to the first grim effort in history to wage war in order to prove the validity of a theory of racial biology.*

Had Lecomte du Noüy's book been the only one of its kind, or had the background of the world order contemporary with it been serene, one might have dismissed it as just another story of a religious conversion, or perhaps have sought to explain it away. The fact that it reported what was going on in the minds of a number of scientists, however dimly and imperfectly they may have formulated their views, and at the same time provided a significant commentary on the riddle as to why humanity should almost have found itself delivered over to abominable masters, made this book the greatest of all tracts for the times. One does not belittle other writers by saying that Lecomte du Noüy was quite incomparably superior, nor does one lessen his contemporaneousness by quoting him: " It must be demonstrated... that, in brief, human dignity is not a vain word, and that when man is not convinced of this and does not try to attain this dignity, he lowers himself to the level of the beast." He had made a long journey through the laboratory and life, and the place to which he had come was high ground. Some others he had long known could not follow him, or perhaps would not. He seemed as alone as a monk in his cell when he wrote: " There is no other way toward human solidarity but the search and respect for individual dignity." That in creating the human brain Evolution had run its course was plain to him. This was indeed its final purpose. Henceforth everything would depend on how man used that brain. He boldly proposed walking in the footsteps of Christ.

Now for the essays in this book. Some of them are concerned with scientific inquiry, its grandeur, and its limitations. Although no individual could foresee what assiduous work in the laboratory would produce in the future, it seemed apparent to Lecomte du Noüy that what is actually the donnée réelle, *the reality the scientists must confront, is that Evolution cannot have proceeded by chance alone. Ideas have unfolded in the Augustinian sense as it progressed. If we suppose that through an as yet undemonstrated combination of compounds a living organism can be made to emerge, that will be the creation of the human intelligence and not the creature of chance. There is also to be found in these reflections on the progress of the biological sciences a secure mastery of the art of historical reflection. For this the nonscientist among his readers will be especially grateful. Because, in spite of his own tireless and fruitful research, he kept his eye fixed on the* grandes lignes, *the contours of the whole of the world and its development, Lecomte du Noüy does not leave his readers bogged down in a welter of detail which they cannot cope with primarily because it fails genuinely to interest them. The nonscientist has no right to castigate the master of the laboratory method for dealing with a subject which for others is a closed book, any more than a professor of English literature can expect to awaken general interest in his effort to explain an obscure sentence in John Donne. But great scientists are not inordinately difficult to follow when they speak on a level of sufficient breadth of their methods, their hypotheses, and their positions.*

However without a doubt the more philosophical and religious essays will prove the most engrossing and exhilarating. The themes are familiar. In describing the science of medicine, " Still embryonic," Lecomte du Noüy foresaw with remarkable clairvoyance what this science would have at its disposal once it could depend upon the development of the other sciences, notably Chemistry. For it is "the most complex of the sciences." And indeed, though mysteries are still with us, for instance that of the origin and control of the dread scourge of cancer, we of the present profit immensely by the convergence of scientific inquiry in the study of human physical well-being. Many will find specially interesting Lecomte du Noüy's respect for intuitions which sometimes come to those who have little technical knowledge. For these pay tribute to the human intelligence, the Supreme Creation of the evolutionary process.

The discussion of religion makes it clear how much Lecomte du Noüy had to overcome before he could recognize with deep conviction the " *perfect model... the awe-inspiring person of Christ.*" *The Church, which professed to be the living continuation of His mission on earth, had opposed and indeed anathematized the scientist. Nothing in this book of essays is more taut in terms of emotion and conviction than are the pages in which Lecomte du Noüy suggests how interpretation of Genesis might bring it into a remarkable consonance with modern biological knowledge. He could not foresee that through its endorsement of Scriptural studies the Second Vatican Council would come close to adopting his interpretation. Perhaps it is not unrealistic to suppose that his views had not a little to do with the outcome. Theologians have changed. I recall that a favorable review of* Human Destiny *written by me in 1947 evoked criticism from those who still believed that the theory of Evolution was a perverse satanic hypothesis. Today no theologian of substance would entertain such an opinion.*

In short, this book, though it reflects the groping of genius toward a solution of fundamental questions and does not, of course, outline the positions which Human Destiny *proposed for general consideration, will prove of the greatest value to those, especially the young, who in their hearts seek a human future like that which Lecomte du Noüy had in mind. Man could, he thought, realize everything which is implicit in his moral endowment. And we must, alas, say that if he does not make the effort because he cannot face the demands made upon his free will, little hope can be held out for mankind. In the end Lecomte du Noüy saw clearly through the dark glass of suffering. His wife says in her biography of him: "As his body wasted away his spirit seemed to radiate ever more brightly around him until even the most cynical left his presence moved to the depths by the shattering experience of contact with a force that their materialism could not explain."*

George N. SHUSTER

TWO LETTERS FROM TEILHARD DE CHARDIN

The following letters from Teilhard de Chardin are of interest because of the evidence they give of the influence of these two Frenchmen on each other's thinking. The first was written to Lecomte du Noüy just before his death in September 1947; the second to Mary Lecomte du Noüy just after her husband's death. The translated texts are presented here by permission of the writer's family.

My dear Friend:

I heard only yesterday from my friend Father LaFarge that you are seriously ill and that you have put yourself completely into the hands of God. This twofold news has moved me deeply for different but related reasons and I want you to know as quickly as possible how much I am thinking of you, how much I am praying for you, and how close I feel to you.

I have often thought of you since our first meeting in 1938, and during the whole war which I spent in Peking. At the end of the hostilities I followed the success of your last books with joy. You were able to deliver your message, *Nunc dimitis*. The whole trend of my thoughts for nearly ten years now, and all the thinking I have done during the recent months since I have been partially immobilized by a slight accident to my health, have reinforced in me the views that are yours and which it was so good to exchange in the past. I would willingly summarize them in the following two propositions:

1) the entire interest and the key of the world are in "Homo-nisation";

2) Christ—when he is well understood in his universal function—is the only true and total homo-nisator.

I would like to have another life so as to devote myself better than I have to the study, the diffusion, and even more to the living reality of this 'Christic Energy'. Thanks to the forces of love which it unleashes in the heart of all the powers of growth and death that exist in the universe it increasingly appears to me—as probably to you also—as the preeminently evolutive principle in a reflective and homonized world. But in reality, the only essential thing, the only thing expected of each one of us, is that we should be in "communion" with this energy in the different nature and aspects it assumes in "what happens"—perhaps after we have done everything possible to have something else happen. With this sole reservation I am very fond of the words that Termier liked to repeat when enduring hard knocks—"Everything that happens is adorable" —and knowing you as I know you my affection finds nothing better to say to you.

Now that the contact is reestablished I hope to have regular news of you through Father LaFarge. I expect to pass the year in Paris. A slight heart attack has, unfortunately, prevented me from going to South Africa this summer. I do not yet know if the hunt for the fossil man will from now on be possible for me. In any case, nothing will prevent me from concentrating all my strength on the study of the "Human Phenomenon".

My respectful and faithful remembrances to your admirable wife who occupies an esteemed place in my memory. Be sure to tell her the deep and complete sympathy which unites me to you in your common hard trial.

May God bless and help you both and may He heal you.

In all faithful friendship.

Signed : P. TEILHARD DE CHARDIN

My dear Madame :

I was profoundly moved and touched by your letter which arrived yesterday. Although Father LaFarge had informed me of your Beloved invalid's frail health, I did not think that his departure was so near, otherwise I would perhaps have written him a little differently. But at any rate he will have felt my sincere attachment and our complete and so remarkable communion of faith.

Now he *knows* and he has rejoined the living and personal heart of that life which he always served so faithfully. Only a few days ago, when writing an article on him and his influence for our periodical *(Les Etudes)*, I was filled with admiration and almost envy for such a full and harmonious existence and also for that extraordinary and rare satisfaction which was given him, thanks to you, of leaving this earth only after he had propounded and promulgated his message; his testimony. In truth he could depart, his life fulfilled—*Nunc dimitis*. Only it is you who remain alone to bear the weight of separation. Oh, you can surely count that I shall transfer to you all the fidelity and warmth of a friendship of which you have always been a part (I hardly separated you from him in my imagination and my thoughts). But above all may his light in a different but just as real guise illumine your life. Little by little a road will certainly open before you which it behooves you to follow so as to rejoin him in a manner worthy of him, and you can be sure that he will help you. It is action in his memory that will console you.

I am well over a little heart trouble that might have been serious, but the doctors still want me to rest until the beginning of December. I do not very well know in what measure I can in the future take up my researches in the field, but I feel that to the end I will continue to develop and defend the views, which were so dear to him also, of a Christianity rejuvenated by the flow of human sap, the eruption of which creates the whole tempest of the world around us. I will probably stay in Paris all year. Many things call me to America, but I do not yet know when I can go there. You will naturally let me know, should you come to Paris.

Thank you again for having written me. God bless you and—in compensation for what He has taken away from you—may He give you the realization of his love and of his presence.

Very respectfully and faithfully.

Signed : P. TEILHARD DE CHARDIN

FOREWORD

This volume contains different articles written by Dr. Pierre Lecomte du Noüy between 1929 and 1945. Some of them have already appeared in magazines. Others were never printed but provided the material for lectures. We have published them in chronological order because in the majority of cases this order is the most logical. In the present case it has the added advantage of enabling us to follow clearly the progressive stages of a line of thought or concept. The first articles deal almost entirely with purely scientific problems. The ardent physicist and biologist underlines the importance of research, proclaims the joys of the laboratory, is moved by the works of some great inventors. But his enthusiasm remains lucid and, because of this lucidity, gradually becomes tinged with scepticism. Can the methods employed by the scientist—the only ones he *can* employ—resolve the essential problem that confronts us; namely, explain the nature of life? We will see that Lecomte du Noüy eventually had to answer this question in the negative. But if science is bound to disappoint us, is there anything else we can fall back upon? The author replies: Yes! All we need is to renew our contact with God. Such an intellectual approach is moving. But can it convince others? I will give a personal opinion further on, but first I would like to summarize the essential points brought out in the following chapters.

Lecomte du Noüy was a physicist by training and inclination and his interest in biology was only aroused by chance. It is not surprising, therefore, that he employed physical methods to solve biological problems. Was he justified in doing this? Undoubtedly he was. The progress of a biological problem depends sooner or later on precise measurements. The author gives us proof of this in the first article : *The Evolution of the Sciences of Life*. For instance: sodium oleate (soap) is soluble in water; its *isomer*, sodium *elaidate*, is not. Their chemical composition is, nevertheless, identical. Yes, but the structure of their elements is not identical and only physics can give us the answer. Then again: the chemical characteristics of a normal serum and those of an immune serum are similar; yet from a physiological point of view these two types of serums have very different properties. How can we discover the reason if not in the last analysis by physical experiments? Biophysics was in its infancy when Lecomte du Noüy made this point in 1929. Today its development is considerable. It cannot be denied that in this case the writer was a good prophet.

The scientific career of Lecomte du Noüy, which started on the battlefields of World War I, in Carrel's laboratory, was continued at the Rockefeller Institute and later on at the Pasteur Institute. In the course of his experiments, Lecomte du Noüy studied the cicatrization of wounds and tissue cultures. His experiments on wounds led him to study the mechanism of cicatrization, and the influence of Carrel awoke his interest in tissue cultures.

He studied the cicatrization of wounds first as a physicist and finally as a philosopher. This led him to propose a measurement of physical time based on units of physiological time. What does this mean? Everyone knows that to evaluate the passage of time we base ourselves on physical time, which is that of our clocks. But does this physical time remain valid when we consider a given individual instead of the world? We all feel, for instance, that time flows more swiftly as we advance in age. One sidereal year "seems" shorter to an old man than to a child. We could argue that this impression is false, but Lecomte du Noüy claims that this would be wrong and provides as proof the precise experiments he made when studying the time needed for wounds to cicatrize in persons of different ages.

The interest of this observation on the physiological plane cannot be denied (hence the interest it raised and still raises among specialists), but can we follow the author when he adds that in the course of 60 minutes of physical time registered by clocks, a child has lived physiologically and psychologically as long as a man of 60 in five hours? This depends on whether we are more or less philosophically inclined.

We must be on our guard, however, as this thesis cannot be rejected offhand. Teachers at least should know about it, for it indicates that masters and pupils may live in worlds where the value of time is radically different. This in itself would explain the difficulty in maintaining the interest of a pupil for more than ten minutes. Lecomte du Noüy comes back to this thesis in his last book, *Human Destiny*. In the present volume it is expressed in two articles: "Ageing" (1933) and "In search of *Intrinsic Human Time*" (1945). Another article is devoted to tissue cultures. Although it was published by Lecomte du Noüy more than thirty years ago it still makes absorbing reading and contains practically no errors.

Scientific research is pursued in laboratories. All those who have lived and worked in them and have felt their special charm will, I am sure, read with pleasure the text devoted to this subject by Lecomte du Noüy.

As I mentioned above, he started his career with complete confidence in the efficacy of this profession. In a way he was right, as he was able to obtain important results in the field of physics. But behind the physicist there lurked a philosopher, and the philosopher ended by realizing that scientific progress is necessarily limited. It is limited by the relative inadequacy of our means of investigation: the senses. It is limited by our methods of experimentation. Finally, it is limited by our ignorance of fundamental processes (Heisenberg's *Principle of Indeterminacy*), which is doubtless definitive.

This conclusion disturbed and even perplexed our physicist. On what can we lean if science, the only guide recognized by superior intellects, is not a sure guide? Faith perhaps? Lecomte du Noüy came to the conclu-

sion that faith (faith in an absolute, namely in God), already present in our moral beliefs, could also be legitimized by the findings of science, and he created his theory of "Telefinalism," which can be summarized in the following manner. Evolution has been decided and willed by God. This evolution, by God's will, resulted in man, not simply in the human form but in the human personality. The masterpiece of creation is the human brain. The ultimate goal is conscience. The brain observes itself. Could this inconceivable but real fact exist if the spirit had not been willed by God? The future of evolution? Man alone is henceforth implicated, but his evolution will not continue in the direction of an anatomical perfection. It will continue solely on the spiritual and intellectual plane. The ultimate end will be a supreme conscience, the domination of the animal instincts by the moral idea. Religion will facilitate and hasten this dominion. Outside of religion there is no salvation. In short, the important thing is not a greater development of the intelligence (the Greeks were as intelligent as we are) but the increase of the moral sense.

Such a concept will certainly please some and displease others. The answer proposed by Lecomte du Noüy has at least the merit of being noble and beautiful. It certainly helped him to live and to die. To live well and to die well. It is always with emotion and a certain uneasiness that I reread the following sentence in the biography that Mme Lecomte du Noüy wrote of her husband: "He often spoke of the help given him by his own theory of telefinalism, but in his dire need theory was rapidly transformed into a more personal faith. From being purely an example, Christ became a living luminous reality, a compassionate spirit that could be prayed to for help. At night when waves of pain engulfed his whole body, I would hear him murmur: "Thy will be done.""

ALBERT DELAUNAY

"Preserve health and cure disease." Ever since its origin medicine has faced these two problems, and it still seeks a scientific solution. The actual state of our medical knowledge leads us to presume that this will take a long time. In its progress through the centuries, however, medicine has been constantly forced to act; has made innumerable trials in the empirical realm and has thus gathered useful information. It has been overrun and confused by all types of systems which disappeared successively because of their fragility but, nevertheless, it has made experiments, acquired ideas, and compiled precious material which will take their place and be of import in scientific medicine later on. The study of life phenomena, both normal and pathological, has progressed surprisingly in our time and continues to progress every day thanks to the development and powerful help of physicochemistry.

"It is therefore evident to every unprejudiced mind that medicine is moving towards its ultimate scientific goal. By the simple, natural march of its evolution it abandons, little by little, the sphere of systems for the analytical form and thus gradually adopts the investigating method common to the experimental sciences."

These lines written by Claude Bernard in 1865 and taken from his brilliant book *Introduction to the Study of Experimental Medicine* received their first striking confirmation in the magnificent work of Pasteur, who by piercing the veil that still shrouded in mystery all the phenomena connected with infectious diseases, enabled medicine to take a great stride forward in one fell swoop. Claude Bernard's own physiological experiments, his studies of certain organic diseases such as diabetes, show to what an extent he had been right.

Nevertheless, these lines could be rewritten even today for they still depict the present state of the question. The task that remains to be accomplished is gigantic, and the information we have acquired concerning the fundamental problems of life is meager in comparison.

It is probable that were Claude Bernard alive he would be surprised by the immense progress accomplished on the one hand in the realm of the exact sciences—physics and chemistry—and on the other hand by the disproportion existing between this progress and that accomplished by the biological sciences. When we scan the vast amount of books and articles written by biologists, physiologists, and doctors in the course of the last sixty years, it seems our knowledge must have increased considerably. But this impression is not confirmed by a critical examination of the results that can be considered as truly acquired. A large number of facts have undoubtedly been assembled and, as Claude Bernard expressed it, "We have acquired notions and compiled precious material which will later have their place and be of import." However, till now this is all that has been accomplished. The fundamental problems, for example those which concern the cell—an element common to all living beings—are not much further advanced than they were in 1865, or even before then. Why? Why has so little light been shed on the elementary phenomena of life during the first quarter of this century which has seen such marvelous progress in physics? Why is it that the most fruitful methods in medicine are still empirical? It seems possible to seek the answer to these questions by studying the relations that exist between medicine and biology in general, and the exact sciences. We will try to do this briefly.

First of all, let us take a general glance. What is biology? Has it evolved and if so in what direction?

Etymologically, biology is the study of life. It therefore covers an immense field. At first it was purely descriptive, applying solely, and for good reason, to the description of phenomena and their order of succession. It has persisted in different forms until our day: natural history, anatomy, cytology, etc. It can be stated that the advent of general biology as a science—in the broadest sense—dates from the fundamental experiments of Lavoisier and Laplace. These great geniuses understood that a science only deserves its name when it establishes quantitative relations between phenomena. They measured the quantity of energy (heat or mechanical) developed in a given time by a living organism and were thus the first to apply the recent notions of chemistry, still in its infancy, to the problems of life which till then had been so mysterious. They succeeded in proving that this quantity of energy corresponds to the quantity liberated by the chemical reactions produced during the same time in the same tissues. This progress was considerable. Measurements had finally penetrated into the realm of life, which thus took its place amongst the subjects that our brain can aim to understand by the light of the other sciences. Biochemistry was born, only a short while after the birth of modern chemistry, and in the same mind. The large number of experiments devoted to the problem since then and all the new discoveries in physics and chemistry have only confirmed Lavoisier's experiments.

The old descriptive biology had no future. If all possible phenomena had been described, would we have been better informed? The most perfect description of the structural, namely the visible elements of the cells, can hardly reveal the deeper mechanisms that must necessarily be known if we wish to understand the underlying reason for a lack of balance or an illness. Beyond the visible perturbations we must discover the phenomena that are the ultimate cause, namely the fundamental chemical and physicochemical phenomena.

We can reach a certain point through descriptive biology (this term includes all the morphological sciences). It takes us as far as the microscope allows it to go and then abruptly abandons us at the very moment when we are faced with the real problem. It cannot be otherwise; for when the eye perceives nothing more, it has exhausted its resources. Many phenomena that have been admirably studied from a morphological and cytological standpoint still contain the final question mark. The intricate mechanism escapes us because it is beyond the reach of the most powerful microscope, because it is not cellular but clearly *molecular*, and therefore chemical. These problems include the ever mysterious problem of the endocrine glands, which regulate the functions of the organism, the appearance of the secondary sexual characters (cockscomb, color of the feathers, spurs) the regrowth of a tentacle amputated from a newt as a consequence of grafting male glands on hens.

Biologists long ago were struck by these facts, and chemistry gradually invaded the realms of biology, physiology, and medicine. The old techniques, in fact, still exist alongside the new and are indispensable to clarify a problem and isolate the important fact or function that needs to be studied chemically. But for many years already, it is chemistry which has been preeminent. Covered by the high authority of Claude Bernard, we can safely affirm that all living functions are nothing more than the remote consequence of the chemical and—we add—physicochemical functions of the molecules which enter into the constitution of each cell. The highest achievement a modern biologist can conceivably aim at is the discovery of the relationship that exists between the structure and the properties of the elementary substances of the cells, humors and tissues of a living organism, and the integral phenomenon resulting from their activities which we call life. This idea did not escape Pasteur, who with the divination of genius had understood the fundamental importance of the molecular dissymmetry in the problems of life at the very beginning of his researches on tartrates and the growth of microorganisms. "The universe," he said one day, "is a dissymmetrical whole. I am inclined to believe that life such as it is manifested to us, must be a function of the dissymmetry of the universe or of the consequences that it entails." He defined his thought still further by saying: "Life is dominated by dissymmetrical actions. I even have the presentiment that in their structure, in their external forms all living species are primarily functions of the cosmic dissymmetry." Unfortunately, Pasteur was engrossed with other problems and could not devote himself to this one, which still remains unsolved.

We will now try to understand the limitations of biochemistry. Chemistry is the science of molecular reactions. It studies the laws which govern the combinations of bodies quantitatively. It analyses by using physical (heat, electricity) or chemical agents to destroy the molecular structures and it synthesizes by rebuilding these structures. It has attained an admirable degree of perfection. The work of Pasteur laid the foundations of stereochemistry, or chemistry in space, which shows us not only the exact elements that constitute bodies but the place occupied in a molecule by each atom in relation to the others as well as the distance which separates one from the other. The particular properties of each body depend not only on its composition but also on the position occupied in space by such a group of atoms. A modern chemist who knows the structural formula of a powerful explosive can establish first on paper and then in the laboratory, the displacements or additions of chemical groups which transform this explosive into a harmless dye or vice versa. He is master of his subject. His methods do not affect the integrity of the substances he treats and in general the original mixture can be reconstituted at any moment with identically the same properties, no matter what the number of dissolutions, precipitations, oxidations or reductions the body he is studying has been subjected to.

For many years scientists believed that this would be equally true for living matter. This was not the case, but it was not discovered right away. Biological chemistry analyzed for years and made important discoveries. It demonstrated the presence in the organism of carbon, nitrogen, hydrogen, oxygen, phosphorus ions, etc. It disclosed and gave the composition of numerous substances indispensable to the equilibrium of life, such as the bilious salts, adrenalin, insulin, amino acids, etc. Every hope seemed justified. But these were merely the *products* of the living cells. The "noble" substances that compose these cells, the ones that are capable of utilizing the nutriments by transforming them chemically, of manufacturing hormones—substances secreted by the glands—of reproducing themselves and of transmitting a nervous influx, were recalcitrant. They refused to let themselves be analyzed with precision and could still less be synthesized: those bodies are the proteins.

When chemistry applied its rather brutal methods to dealing with these proteins, which are the fundamental elements of living matter, of protoplasm, cells, and blood, it killed them. Just as a blacksmith, after destroying a gramophone with a hammer, attempts afterwards to reconstruct it by putting together the remains of wood, copper, zinc, and rubber, but cannot recover the voice of Caruso, so chemistry is helpless when faced by the wreck of the fragile and marvelous giant molecule that has not yielded its secret.

Everywhere scientists were brought to a stop by the same insufficiency of means. Not only was synthesis out of the question but often analysis, though highly sensitive, was also found wanting. We now know, for instance, that species differ chemically, that horse albumin is not identical to dog albumin; but we became convinced of this through biological and not through chemical methods, and we do not know the *real* difference between the two albumins. Not only the different species but individuals of a same species differ chemically. It is impossible to transfuse any type of blood into a patient with impunity, without fear of accident. This is a fact of observation; nothing more. That important protein hemoglobin which craves oxygen and transports this gas into our entire arterial system, can be obtained in the pure crystalline state. But the crystals differ in aspect from one animal to another. This is the absolute proof of a difference in their chemical nature, but no one has ever been able to agree on the composition or structure of this body for no one knows how and why hemoglobins differ from one another. Everybody knows that immunity is a property conferred on an animal or a person which enables them to fight successfully against the toxins transported or secreted by microbes. It is also known that this condition can be put in evidence by certain biological reactions which indicate that "something has been changed" in the

8

individual concerned. Chemistry, however, can discover no difference.

A subject is bled. The serum exuded by his coagulated blood floats on top and is analyzed by all possible methods. Two hours later a cubic centimeter of his own serum is reinjected into the individual. There is no reaction. But if he is reinjected the next day he experiences a shock, and if the injections are persisted with the "shock" can become very serious with a sudden fall of pressure, a fall of temperature, etc. Chemical analysis reveals no difference between the fresh serum and the one that is several days old. Yet the latter is toxic while the other is harmless.

And what a number of other questions remain unanswered: blood coagulation, ferments, all the problems connected with the nervous systems, to name but a few. We know that in the final analysis we will only be satisfied by a chemical, molecular, or atomic explanation. But we are forced to admit that pure chemical methods are insufficient or inadequate.

Why? Undoubtedly for many different reasons, but principally because the proteins which compose living matter are characterized by an unbelievable fragility which may account for certain of their curious properties. The chemist who attacks proteins soon discovers that he cannot manipulate these bodies like the others—the oils, greases, alcohols, sugars, dyes, explosives—nor can he, as we said above, stop the operations at any stage and proceed in an inverse direction if he is so inclined. Far from finding the components of a complex product intact after having oxidized, reduced, precipitated, or dissolved them, he finds that any operation of this kind definitively destroys something in the body he is treating. In other words, the modifications he produces in these bodies are irreversible. Most reactives, like heat or even time, affect proteins in such a way that they are no longer the same: they are denatured. We therefore do not know the exact original composition of these substances. Each molecule probably consists of 4 000 or 8 000 atoms, and they are so fragile that they only exist in particular conditions that are often undetermined. The problem seems inextricable.

About thirty years ago, a certain number of biologists threw themselves wholeheartedly into the study of chemistry which appeared to be the source of all truth. They were followed by a few, far too rare chemists who threw themselves into biology. At that time they did not know that though the solution of their problem had to be chemical, chemistry, such as we know it, could not give them the answer. Their reasoning was simple : chemical problems, therefore chemical methods. They did not know that the bodies they wanted to study escaped the rules followed by the inorganic bodies, the lowest in the hierarchy of matter. The result was unforeseen and rather surprising for the pure chemists. Every time a biochemist encountered a difficulty, a singular and baffling property of the substances he was handling, he immediately invented a new body to explain it and gave it a lovely name. The "complement," the "sensitizer," the "antibody," and many other entities thus appeared. In spite of their always hypothetical existence they were useful by momentarily simplifying the language and, as human genius is sometimes immense, some very important practical discoveries resulted therefrom; the Bordet —Jengou reaction, for example, known in a special case as the Wasserman reaction. But at bottom the problem remained as obscure as on the first day, and we have hardly progressed.

Does this mean that we must give up the struggle and say with Du Bois-Reymond: *Ignorabimus*? Far from it. Nowadays we can call other sciences to the rescue; sciences that have attained a prodigious degree of perfection. Their methods are remarkably delicate and sensitive and allow us to respect the integrity of the mysterious and fragile edifice represented by a protein molecule. We have named physics and its younger sister physicochemistry.

What in brief is physics? It is a combination of methods and observations that have enlarged the scope of our senses far beyond their normal sphere. The range of our perceptions is limited by the sharpness of our senses which are restricted and often inferior to that of animals. For instance, physics has enabled us, directly or indirectly, to attain and measure the dimensions of molecules that are a million times smaller

than the smallest object that can be seen by our eye. But this is not all. The human eye reacts to certain radiations called "lightwaves," which extend from deep red (wavelength 0.8 thousandth of a millimeter) to violet (wavelength 0.4 thousandth of a millimeter). All our visible universe is contained in this minute scale of 0.4 thousandth of a millimeter. Other radiations exist on either side. Physics has enabled us not only to study and measure them but to utilize them. It has therefore enlarged our universe, has given us antennae often more sensitive than our senses and has united in a continuous range all the radiations, from the radio waves, 30 kilometers in length, to those of X-rays, 1 tenmillionth of a millimeter in length. Today there are no more "gaps" in the series of waves.

At the base of our knowledge of matter we find the atom. The atoms of simple elements are combined to make up the molecules of compound bodies. The small molecules, admirably analyzed by chemistry, are well known, and the fact that physics has been able to photograph the arrangement of the atoms at the interior of crystals by means of X-rays has enabled us to know them even better. It was thus possible to check mathematically the exactitude of the structural formula. But the very large molecules are endowed with special properties and there exist classes of bodies which cannot be thus dissected| by X-rays. They are the colloids to which all the proteins belong. Their fragility which we mentioned above is due precisely to the dimensions and the complexity of these bodies.

We know that the properties of a body depend not only on its chemical composition but also on the way its atoms are disposed in space. Sodium oleate (soap) is soluble in water; its isomer, sodium elaïdate, with an identical composition but a different structure, is insoluble. We can therefore understand how the properties of a molecule can vary in proportion to its volume, namely its complication, without its composition being changed. But then we begin to perceive a new reason why pure chemistry when it demolishes a protein molecule can find no difference between a normal serum and an immunized serum, for instance. This may be due to a difference in structure. Chemistry can distinguish structural differences in relatively uncomplicated, stable molecules. But it is powerless when faced by several thousand atoms and irreversible, unstable bodies. Furthermore when we study the solutions of the huge protein molecules [1] we discover that some forces enter into play that are not chemical forces. These molecules agglomerate without the intervention of a true reaction. Not only do they agglomerate, thus forming what are called "micellae," but they adsorb other smaller molecules, namely fix them solidly to their surface. It is evident that the proteins do not group themselves haphazardly. Their structure imposes certain positions. It has been proved recently that they have a tendency to orient themselves, to agglomerate, following certain axes. The immediate result is that the chemical groups that are on the surface that is fixed are neutralized whereas those that are at the extremities have a maximum activity in a minimum space. Likewise, a handful of matches bound closely together with their phosphorus ends touching will explode violently if one of the matches is lighted, but if they are placed on a table in no particular order they will burn slowly, one by one, with a small isolated explosion occurring from time to time when the flame reaches them. Another very important consequence of this tendency to orient themselves in a solution is the formation of electric condensers of molecular dimensions which probably play a primordial part in the exchanges between membranes, in the transmission of nervous reflexes, and in all biological mechanisms in general.

Numerous problems will probably find their explanation in the physical forces themselves as well as in their influence on the chemical reactions of the proteins. Only the most sensitive and recent physical methods enable us to study them. We have already insisted on the fact that these methods have the advantage of respecting the integrity of the molecular

1. This immensity is relative of course: an ovalbumin molecule measures around 41 hundred millionths of a centimeter in length and contains nearly 1 400 carbon atoms and 2 250 hydrogen atoms. The wavelength of the smallest visible light radiation is a hundred times greater.

structure. They destroy nothing. Doubtless we do not always know how to interpret the information they give us, but we are only at the beginning of these experiments and we are daily learning how to utilize them and adapt them to special cases.

We can ask ourselves how the transition from physics to chemistry is brought about. The answer is simple. Chemistry studies the combinations of atoms and molecules. Physical methods have led us to conceive an atom as a miniature solar system where the sun is represented by the central nucleus carrying a positive electric charge and the planets by the electrons, or negative electric particles, turning at great speed around this nucleus. Now the number of these electrons, and the number of their orbits are known, and the chemical properties of the atom depend on these as well as on the value of the charge of the positive nucleus. As, furthermore, it has been possible to apply certain mechanical laws to these systems and in some cases to calculate the heat developed in a reaction, while taking into account only the mechanical and physical properties of the electrons of each atom, we can realize that these sciences, molecular and atomic physics, are really at the base of modern chemistry and, consequently, ultimately at the base of the sciences of life.

From the preceding facts it would seem that the problem was clearly put, and that we can logically admit that living matter must reveal its secrets as soon as the chemistry of proteins has finally been established through the help of physics. In addition, however, to all the difficulties already enumerated there is, alas, another—formidable yet passionately interesting—which we will now examine.

What, in short, does every physical law consist of? It consists of a proposition that describes as briefly as possible the evolution of a phenomenon or the sequence of a series of phenomena in time. Physical laws are all global and on our scale. In other words, they admit that a great number of molecules are present and participate in the phenomena. To take an example: the law of falling bodies implies the fall of a body, namely of a mass of molecules; the law of communicating vessels establishes the "obvious" fact that two masses of gas contained in two communicating vessels will develop the same pressure: the law of Mariotte, etc.

In the case of the two vessels filled with gas a simple reasoning leads to the conclusion that until the pressures attain equilibrium the more numerous molecules contained in one of the vessels will have a tendency to pass into the other. Afterwards the mean number of molecules passing from one vessel into the other will be the same in both directions; hence equality of the mean number of shocks per unity of surface and equality of pressure. Fluctuations are negligible. It is a law of averages, a *statistical* law based on an immense number of molecules.

But what would happen if the communicating vessels were so small that they could only contain a few molecules of gas? The probability that the number of molecules would be equal in each vessel would be slight. As soon as, by a chance shock in the direction of the opening, one molecule passes from vessel No. 1 into vessel No. 2, the pressure in the latter is higher until another molecule passes by chance into vessel No. 1. It is clear that if the number of molecules is very small, the division in equal parts will not always be obtained, In other words the pressures will only be equal exceptionally. The conditions are therefore very different. In the case of vessels of "ordinary" dimensions it is of no importance if the number of molecules in each vessel is not the same. The immense total number of molecules renders the inequality absolutely imperceptible. In a vessel of a liter, at ordinary pressure, there are about 27,000,000,000,000,000,000,000 molecules.[1] The chances that one of the vessels contains 1 percent more molecules than the other are extremely slight, for 1 percent represents much more than two hundred billion billion molecules. This inequality corresponds to a fluctuation that is evidently very improbable. On the other hand, an excess of 100, or even 1000, molecules on one side will not make itself felt, for it would only correspond to a difference in pressure impossible to measure. The law is based therefore, like all present scientific laws, on the existence of

1. 27 Thousand billion billion in franeo-american usage.

an immense number of molecules. If there are no more than 10 molecules in each vessel and a single one passes from one vessel to another, as is very probable, there will be a change of pressure of 10 per cent. The law is no longer exact: we enter into a new realm, that of the individual actions of the molecules, where the fluctuations, namely the deviations with respect to the mean phenomenon become important. This realm is ultramicroscopic, it is true, but are not the elements of the organisms and certain organisms themselves ultramicroscopic?

Does this mean that all our modern science becomes inapplicable on this scale? Is this the maximum value that can be attributed to its laws? Undoubtedly, for we must not overlook the fact that they have been created by the infirmities and limitations of our senses. Nevertheless, such as they are, they are of immense service, for they correspond to our universe. But if we knew the elementary laws of the atoms and molecules, we would have no use for the statistical laws, the laws of current physics, that we apply daily.

And without looking any further do we not know that the world of a very small insect, a plant louse for instance, must be very different from ours?

In brief, as Professor Charles E. Guye, one of the most distinguished thinkers of our epoch, admirably stated: "it is essentially the scale of observation that creates the phenomenon". We must, therefore, take into account *the difference in scale* which is capable of upsetting all our physics including to a certain degree the fundamental principles such as the Carnot law. Might not the privilege of living organisms to escape the laws that are decreed general by our pride, lie in precisely this fact? Helmholtz was the first to consider this problem which is of capital importance.

Here an objection can be raised: all this may only be a theory. Has a biological phenomenon that can only be explained by such arguments ever been observed? Yes, in a virulent culture of microbes. A microbe is isolated and cultivated separately. As soon as it has reproduced itself and has divided in two, each part is again cultivated separately until there are about ten pure cultures proceeding from the same original culture. These cultures are then injected into ten animals and we observe that out of the ten animals injected a certain number do not manifest any pathological phenomena, whereas the others develop all the characteristics of the disease and die (Bronfenbrenner experiments). What happened? A *sudden mutation* which can hardly be explained except by the reasoning based on the ideas expounded above and on the preponderant part that can be played by an important fluctuation at a given moment.

There would be no problem if heredity depended on the play of a considerable number of identical elements. The average laws excluding all mutations would apply or rather make them less probable. The appearance of these mutations indicates, on the contrary, that we are in the presence of too slight a number of elements. It is a case that is analogous to the very small communicating vessels we mentioned above; the displacement of one molecule invalidates the statistical law.

We realize that all the problems of life, of evolution even, are at stake and that we do not yet possess the necessary factors to attack them fruitfully. For the present, we need not preoccupy ourselves with the problem of replacing our old statistical laws by molecular and atomic laws of individual action. There is still a tremendous task to be accomplished by means of the present material and intellectual tools.

Molecular biophysics is still young and the chemistry of proteins is in its infancy. The study of the superficial equilibria of solutions, of the monomolecular layers, of proteins, of the orientation of the molecules; the perfecting and development of methods of analysis by X-rays, the use of a great number of marvelous instruments restricted with rare exceptions to laboratories of pure physics, and the systematic utilization of the remarkable techniques of Carrel for the culture of tissues *in vitro* will certainly enable us to make great strides in the knowledge of living matter.

Physical methods have not yet borne much fruit, but they have rarely been employed methodically for there are still very few laboratories in existence that are devoted to these experiments.

Scientific workers cannot be of service to medicine at the present stage of our knowledge of living matter. Our ignorance of the chemistry of proteins prevents us from grasping the real cause of pathological disturbance. Behind the causes that we know, as we said above, there is always another deeper cause that will escape us as long as we have not advanced in the study of the most elementary phenomena of cellular life. A day will probably come in the distant future, when the study of a drop of blood plasma or of an organic secretion in the laboratory will enable us to give a rigorous diagnosis of the origin of the instability and to apply a logical, precise and efficacious therapy. It is clear that progress will advance in this direction if nothing occurs to interrupt its course.

It is equally evident that practical medicine is alone capable of fulfilling the immediate needs of humanity, and must continue to study illnesses with the help of clinical laboratories along with the long-range research of biochemists and biophysicists.

Let us now try to summarize and conclude. First of all we showed to what degree all the sciences interpenetrate each other nowadays and in particular how biology and medicine closely depend on physics, chemistry, and even mechanics. Strange as it may seem at first sight, the grave and distressing problem of cancer probably entails in the last analysis a physical solution of molecular and atomic interaction.

Tomorrow's *general biology* therefore depends on a collaboration between biologists and first class specialists: physicists, chemists, even mathematicians passionately interested in the same problem. This necessity understandably entails numerous difficulties both of a moral and material order, and as a result these fundamental problems, on which the medicine of the future depends, are the most neglected. The most evident difficulties are those that have sprung from this necessity to collaborate and especially to coordinate the efforts of several scientists. This is a highly complex and delicate problem.

The difficulties that arise in second place are due to the financial troubles arising from actual living conditions. A certain courage is needed to dedicate oneself to these questions for the soil is, so to speak, virgin. It is the jungle where no one has yet penetrated and the vocation of pioneer is not very prevalent in these days when it is so hard to satisfy material needs. The man who takes the risk can lose ten or twenty years of his life without making a single important discovery; without advancing one step. Yet he must devote himself entirely to his task. Thus if he has a family and children it is out of the question, for he must live.

In general, young laboratory workers receive low salaries and can only depend on themselves for their sources of joy. All those without independent means who nevertheless consecrate themselves to scientific research possess the sacred fire that Pasteur so loved and represent a true elite. There are a few, but not enough. The funds assigned to a large laboratory in a provincial faculty, directed by a distinguished scientist, were so small that not only was it impossible to acquire any instruments but there was not even enough money to feed the experimental animals, the rabbits and chickens. Three pupils, who had difficulty in nourishing themselves, and the laboratory assistant (at a salary of 600 Francs a month) clubbed together to pay it. But out of a hundred young men who finish their scientific training more than ninety go into industry. Amongst these are many brillant minds who would be of great benefit to pure science, i.e. true progress, and every means should be employed to enroll them.

New, richly endowed research institutes to be at the forefront of progress should therefore be created. Perhaps for lack of better information the public is only interested in undertakings capable of producing immediate results. It does not know or, prefers to ignore, that these results are often without real scientific interest and contribute nothing to the advancement of our knowledge. Money is contributed without stint to humanitarian projects that appeal to the imagination and the heart, but which only have a momentary social value in the most favorable cases. And yet there will be more glory in the future for those who, having understood the new needs before the majority, will have helped and encouraged the first efforts of researchers in a purely scientific path. It is the only path capable of laying the unshakeable foundations for the medicine of the future which will one day enable it to fight victoriously against disease, no longer blindly but with full knowledge of the facts.

TISSUE CULTURE IN VITRO 1931

I have already tried to show why biologists, when studying the phenomena of life, must resort increasingly to the so-called exact sciences;
physics, chemistry, and physicochemistry. I tried to explain the reasons
why pure, organic chemistry alone could not solve all problems and to
outline the advantages of physicochemical and other methods, such as
the culture of tissues outside the organism. Dr. Alexis Carrel not only
created this last method, but brought it to a high point of perfection.
At present it is the only general biological method that can be compared
with the exact sciences because it permits measurements, and a phenomenon is only really known when we are able to measure it. All
sciences, still in their infancy, such as biology and medicine, tend
towards this distant goal.

To understand fully the progress brought about by the method of
tissue cultures *in vitro*, it is necessary to give a short outline of the methods
employed up till now to study living matter—the tissues and their constituent elements, the cells. This study constitutes a science—cytology—
which has reached an advanced stage of development, but which
has neglected the most important factors of the problem, namely
the function of the cells. In other words, their reason for existence.
Indeed, cytology limited itself to the morphological examination of

dead cells by means of the microscope. It is a static method and the opposite of the culture of tissues, which is essentially kinetic and dynamic. Cytology describes the aspect of the internal elements of the cells, in great detail, after the latter have been killed by different reactives and dyed by means of special substances. It is incapable, however, of explaining the most ordinary pathological phenomenon, such as the cicatrization of a wound or the growth of a tumor.

A recent article by Dr Carrel develops these ideas strikingly.

The structure of tissues and their functions, are two aspects of the same thing. One cannot consider them separately. Each structural detail possesses its functional expression. It is through the physiological aptitudes of their anatomical parts, that the life of the higher animals is rendered possible. Likewise, the life of a community of ants depends on the physiological aptitudes of the individuals of which it is composed. When cells are considered only as structural elements, they are deprived of all the properties that make them capable of organizing as a living whole. Within the organism, they are associated according to certain laws. Cell sociology is the result of properties specific to each type of cell. Among these properties, some manifest themselves under ordinary conditions of life, while others remain hidden and only enter into play when certain modifications of the internal environment occur, as for instance, when pathogenic agencies are at work within the body. The significance of a given structural state is bound to the knowledge of the corresponding physiological state. Structure and function must be considered simultaneously.

Furthermore, tissues evolve in time. A tissue consists of a society of complex organisms, which does not respond in an instantaneous manner to the changes of the environment. It may oppose such changes for a long time before adapting itself through slight or deep transformations. To study it at only one instant of its duration is almost meaningless. The temporal extension of a tissue is as important as its spatial existence.

In other words, if I may be forgiven a trivial comparison, it is not by observing and dissecting the corpses in the morgue that we can hope to understand the economic life of the city of Paris. In brief, the conception of cells and tissues which Carrel has substituted for the classical viewpoint is that of a system: cell environment, of which the structural, functional, physical, physicochemical and chemical conditions are considered in time as well as in space. It is evident that a radical transformation of method was necessary to renovate cytology in accord with this ideal. Since 1912, Dr Carrel has applied himself to this task, with striking success.

The method he developed is called *tissue culture in vitro*. It enables one to maintain fragments of tissue alive outside the organism. These fragments are preferably cut out of an embryo, such as the embryo of a chicken. They grow actively in an appropriate medium and possess the faculty of living indefinitely. The descendants of the original cells in a small piece of chicken heart extracted in 1912 are still alive today after nineteen years and shows no signs of ageing; namely, its growth activity is the same as at the beginning. Barring accidents, there is no reason why it should ever die. It is superfluous to add that had the chicken from which it was extracted, lived its normal life, it would have been dead long ago. Ten years constitutes about the extreme limit of duration of a chicken's existence.

Different workers, especially Harrison, had tried before Carrel to maintain pieces of tissue alive outside the organism. But no one succeeded in prolonging the life of these explanted fragments beyond a few days, for lack of proper nourishment. They therefore obtained only a momentary survival and not a continuous existence which, though not normal, is at least very active. This is the advantage of Dr Carrel's method. He was the first person to prevent death from setting in, and this is precisely the fundamental point of the method. The explanted tissues, which are kept in special containers with tremendous aseptic precautions, as one single microbe suffices to infect the culture and to kill it, can be assimilated to immortal experimental animals. It is therefore possible to experiment indefinitely on the same family of cells proceeding from the same strain. This results in a greater precision because of the elimination of innumerable causes of errors due to the individual characteristics of animals of different origin. But this is not the only advantage inherent in this method.

To preserve these tissues, they must be divided into two equal part at short intervals, generally every forty-eight hours. Indeed, "fibroblast" cultures or conjunctive tissue cells, which are very prevalent in all organisms, double their volume in two days. In certain cases the cultures are allowed to grow for two or three weeks and then attain a size of about one square centimeter. By thus dividing a culture, its nourishment can take place on the surface (as it has no circulating system) and it can eliminate the toxic products resulting from the selection it makes in the nutritive substances that are given it. Washing in a special solution facilitates this elimination. Two cultures rigorously identical from a biological point of view are thus available, instead of one. Consequently, for each experiment and for every stage of the experiment, the operator disposes of a "witness". For all biological experiments it is important to have one or several controls on which no experiment has been made, in order to appreciate the results obtained on the experimental animal by comparison. But two animals are never identical, hence causes of error, whereas two parts of the same culture are obviously as identical as possible.

Furthermore, to study the characteristics and properties of certain species of microbes it is necessary to dispose of pure cultures; i.e., free from all foreign organisms. It is quite evident that when there is a mixture of different microbes it is impossible to define the function of each species in the lesions and accidents determined in an animal by the culture. It would be impossible to prepare a vaccine or curative serum against one of these organisms. This is equally true of tissue cultures. To be able to study the cytological and physiological characteristics of a certain species of cells, it is necessary to obtain pure cultures. First Carrel and then, under his direct guidance, Fischer, Ebeling, and others, succeeded in isolating pure strains of fibroblasts, osteoblasts, epithelium, and cancer cells. These strains are generally capable of living indefinitely *in vitro* while conserving all their specific characteristics. This discovery was not accepted without a struggle by certain biologists, particularly in France, who pretended that it was impossible—simply because their own imperfect techniques had prevented them from succeeding. These facts are now classical and no longer discussed by anyone.

We have used the word "technique" and we will now say a few words on the subject. A "technique" as everyone knows, is the combination of all the material methods employed to obtain a certain experimental result. The subject of tissue culture techniques is vast enough to fill a voluminous book and I shall therefore make a very brief summary. The principle is simple. It consists of cutting out a fragment of tissue and incorporating it in a medium capable of sustaining it (coagulum) and of nourishing it at the same time. The products of excretion are eliminated by washing every other day and replanting (in other words, transplanting) the culture into a new medium. The cultures are naturally maintained at the temperature which is normal for the animal from which they proceed.

Realization is less simple. Indeed, as I have already stated, it was Dr Carrel who discovered the nutritive medium capable of indefinitely prolonging the life of the cells; this medium is the *embryonic juice*. It is obtained by mincing eight-day-old chicken embryos and mixing the pulp thus obtained with a complex saline solution. This mixture, centrifuged and decanted, is the embryonic juice, which no one, so far, has been able to replace by any synthetic medium. But infinite aseptic precautions must be taken in preparing this *juice*—far greater than for any surgical operation. Great chemical and physicochemical precautions must also be taken when preparing the saline solutions (Ringer and Tyrode solutions). The substances employed must be rigorously pure and the degree of alkalinity (measured by the concentration in hydrogen ions expressed by the symbol pH) must be controlled electrically or colorimetrically.

So much for the *juice*. But there is also the *support*, which is composed of a drop of coagulated chicken plasma. The culture itself, about one or two square millimeters in size, is placed in this drop, or on its surface, according to the nature of the cells cultivated. We remind the reader that blood is composed of red and white corpuscles suspended in a liquid called the *plasma*. The blood is taken by operating on a young and healthy chicken under anesthesia, and the plasma is separated from the corpuscles by centrifugation in tubes previously treated with paraffin, so as to prevent premature coagulation, and which are naturally sterile.

When these elements have been prepared, all that remains to be done is to take an incubated egg about ten days old, remove the embryo, aseptically of course, dissect the heart or any other part of the animal, cut out a certain number of pieces and incorporate them on a thin mica slide into a drop of plasma mixed with a drop of *embryonic juice*. The mica is then covered by a thick glass slide hollowed out in the middle, sealed with paraffin, and put into an incubator at 38º C. Forty-eight hours later the fragments are taken out, cut, washed in Tyrode solution, and "replanted"—in other words, incorporated into a new coagulated nutritive drop and so on. The small pieces of heart rapidly surrounded by a transparent circle of new cells, often continue to beat for two or three weeks. They can be seen to contract periodically, forty or fifty times a minute outside the organism and nothing is more impressive than to thus observe the working of this marvelous and still so mysterious mechanism.

Tissue culture is neither simple nor easy when pure strains have to be maintained in good health for any length of time. Nothing is easier than to maintain them for two or three weeks. The difficulties come later and it requires a long experience to be able to prolong their existence beyond two or three months. One must be a good "culture doctor" to diagnose at a glance a fatty degeneration or a variation in the shape of the cells that indicates an impaired health. The treatment to be applied differs according to the case, and there are no precise rules. Everything depends on the experience, one can almost say the "clinical" sense, of the operator. This explains why very few laboratories, perhaps three or four, possess old strains of pure cultures. The material organization of such laboratories is not very complicated, but the difficulties arise principally from the rigorous care that must be given to the technique in detail and to sterilization.

The development of this new science depends entirely on the possibility of maintaining the principal types of cells in a state of pure cultures. Carrel was the first to demonstrate that this was possible. The study of these cultures has revealed that each cellular type is characterized not only by its morphological aspect but also by an aggregate of special physiological properties. These properties remained unknown up till now because they were hidden by the tremendous complexity of the phenomena which take place in the organism. It is impossible to know the physiological state of the cells and, consequently, the significance of what is observed if cells extracted from a living animal or derived from impure cultures—mixtures of cells of different specie—are studied by means of the old techniques as still practiced by Lewis, Burrows, Loeb, Champy, Drew, Borrel, etc. It is only by means of colonies composed of a single type of cell, placed in flasks containing a medium of known composition and manifesting a measurable form of activity, that it becomes possible to establish a relation between the morphological state (as seen under the miscroscope) and the functional state of thet cells.

"The task of the new cytology," writes Carrel, "is to discover the physiological properties which characterize each type of cell. It is impossible to attempt the study of these properties by any other method than that of pure cultures. It is the only method which enables us to introduce precise modifications in the conditions of life of the colonies and to show up the potentialities which often remain hidden during the normal life of a cell. Bacteriologists are not content to study the shape and the reactions of microbes in connection with certain dyes, but they also examine the aspect of their colonies, their action on the culture medium, the poisons they secrete, their susceptibility to different antiseptics, the nutritive substances they require, etc. The same is true of tissue cells. Today we can identify these cells, not only by their structure and the reactions of their organs to dyes, but by the appearance of their colonies, their mutual reactions, their mode of locomotion as recorded by cinematography, their effect on the coagulum of the medium, their rate of growth, the nature and the concentration of the substances that are toxic for them, the nature of the substances that produce their multiplication, etc.

"The new cytology permits the identification of cells and the prediction of their conduct under given conditions. It reveals the specific properties of each type of cell. Thanks to this new cytology the mechanism of complex phenomena, which takes place in normal or pathological tissues, can be submitted to experimental analysis. Its fecundity will be necessarily greater than that of the classic cytology."

The culture of tissues has already considerably increased our knowledge of cell physiology, and we are only at the beginning of this study. It is obvious that this method will be extremely fruitful in the hands of the new generation of biologists.

Besides the fundamental, classical problems that can be attacked by this method, it will certainly reveal, and has already revealed, new problems that we might always have ignored without it. I will give a very suggestive example—

We have seen that the fragments of muscular tissue removed from the heart of a chicken embryo frequently continue to beat in the culture. When two of these palpitating fragments proceeding from the same heart are put next to each other, but without touching, their rhythm is generally not identical. One fragment beats eighty times a minute for instance, the other fifty. Should it so happen, which is rare, that their pulsations are identical, they are nevertheless not synchronous. But these fragments proliferate and gradually surround themselves with a circle of new cells, which penetrate into the medium in the shape of a thin, translucent, living layer. After a certain length of time, these fine membranes issued from the two fragments, come into contact; at that very moment *the rhythm becomes identical*. The synchronism is reestablished; the two fragments beat as one. Thus, though the bird has been long dead, though the small pieces of muscle separated from its heart have neither blood circulation nor a nervous system connected to a main trunk, they persist, if they are in contact, in accomplishing the work for which they were created by contracting periodically, not in a haphazard independent fashion, but together and coordinately. Needless to say, there is not the beginning of an explanation for this curious phenomenon.

Another example—a single *isolated* cell does not proliferate—it dies without dividing in two even though it appears to be identically in the same conditions as the healthy culture from which it has been separated and which proliferates rapidly. Cellular growth and multiplication require the presence of a certain number of cells in the same medium. In brief, everything occurs as if certain substances secreted by the cells were required to set free the mechanism of the other cells. What are these substances? What is the mechanism? All these problems are still very mysterious.

We have insisted on the necessity of employing pure cultures composed of a single type of cell. This is a capital point, but also the most delicate one of the method. Its importance was not fully realized by many workers who, at the start, were filled with enthusiasm by the possibilities which they foresaw. Some of them, when they finally understood, were soon discouraged by the meticulous care, the patience, the staff and the technical equipment required to conduct constructive experiments successfully. In our laboratory at the Pasteur Institute, three people are occupied from morning until evening, all the year round, in isolating and maintaining these strains and this is a minimum number. At the Rockefeller Institute, Dr Carrel employs about fifteen assistants and women technicians for this task.

Experiments can be conducted only with cultures at least three months old. At that age, they constitute relatively homogeneous units. They can then be submitted to different diets so that a study can be made either of their morphological modifications, their physiological reactions, or alterations in their mobility.

We will give a few examples of morphological and physiological modifications. They can be reversible as, for instance, alterations of the structures or dimensions of the cells and of their elements; or irreversible, such as the transformation of one type of cell into another. Certain cells develop only in groups and form tissues (fibroblasts, epithelium, etc.). Others, on the contrary, are independent and invade the culture medium like children let loose in the courtyard of a school. Leucocytes (white cells) and one of their varieties—macrophages—are in this category. The latter are found almost everywhere in the organism—in blood, in lymph, in bone marrow, and in conjunctive tissue. They are phagocytes; that is to say they envelop, then digest solid particles, microbes among others. When cultivated in plasma, macrophages transform themselves into large cells surrounded by an undulating membrane. The addition of certain substances such as amino peptones and organic enzymes brings about the disappearance of these membranes and the transformation of the mobile cells into fixed cells. But these changes are reversible. The undulating membranes reappear after a few days in an appropriate medium. On the other hand, when an extract of Rous sarcoma (spontaneous chicken cancer) is added to a culture of macrophages, the cells are *transformed into fibroblasts*. The same is true of fibroblasts treated with plasma containing heparin (a substance which prevents plasma from coagulating). The fibroblasts turn into macrophages and these changes are *irreversible*. The fibroblasts acquire all the physiological properties of the macrophages and conserve them.

A culture does not completely cease growing when it is made to fast.

Its life is slowed down, however, and the conditions resemble more closely the normal conditions in the organism. But its activity is then manifested in other ways. The cells function *physiologically*—in other words, they accomplish the same tasks which they fulfill in the organism and secrete the substances which they normally produce. In our laboratories where a pure liver culture had been isolated, it had been noticed that the well-fed cells no longer manufactured "glycogene," a substance which transforms itself into sugar (glucose) and is one of the more important products normally elaborated by this organ. When, however, the liver culture had been submitted to a reduced diet by suppressing the *embryo juice* the glycogenic functions started working again, exactly as in the organism.

The same phenomenon was observed with the pigment cells of the iris of the eye. When too well nourished, the cells proliferated abundantly but without producing pigment or coloring matter. When subjected to a diet, they ceased growing in number but secreted the black pigment which characterizes them *in vivo*.

It is evident that this method is particularly adapted to the study of cancer. It suffices to compare pure cultures proceeding from malignant tumors to cells of the same type but devoid of malignancy. It was thus soon ascertained that macrophages proceeding from "Rous sarcoma" are unhealthy, abnormal cells which degenerate rapidly and do not live long. They require the same nourishment as normal macrophages, but unlike the latter they actively digest the coagulum. On the other hand, the fibroblasts proceeding from another cancer, the "Crocker No. 10," are strong, healthy cells and require the same nourishment as normal fibroblasts, but they also digest the coagulum. Epithelial cells from the Ehrlich carcinoma are unhealthy, delicate cells like those of the Rous sarcoma. They likewise digest the coagulum.

Other types of malignant cells have been studied and it was found that no matter how divergent they are on certain points, they all have properties in common; such as this faculty of digesting and liquefying the solid part of the coagulum—the fibrin. Furthermore, they can assimilate

31

substances which do not nourish normal cells. It is therefore possible to conclude, as does Dr Carrel, that cancerous cells acquire their malignancy *in vivo* because of their faculty for manufacturing nutritive substances from the surrounding tissues and fluids. This enables them to proliferate in an unlimited fashion. The mutability of certain types of cells, of which we have spoken above, takes on all its importance at this point. Malignant cells are varieties of normal types, from which they differ only slightly through certain properties. These differences are not qualitative, but quantitative and irreversible. After several years of culture *in vitro*, they have not regressed to the original type. They are fixed varieties.

The hypothesis of the microbic nature of cancer has been abandoned as a result of these experiments and of many others, which we cannot describe for lack of space. Unfortunately, the knowledge thus obtained

has not yet resulted in any practical progress towards the eradication of this scourge. But these researches are in their infancy and every hope is permissible. Dr Albert Fischer will soon have an institute in Copenhagen given over entirely to tissue cultures which has been completely financed by the Rockefeller Institute. His latest remarkable experiments are a good omen for the future.

The almost unlimited applications of this method are easy to conceive. Thanks to it, we can study the problems of immunity *in vitro*. A tissue behaves like an organism and reacts against the poisoning due to the toxic substances carried by microbes by manufacturing the specific antidote substance; called antibodies. Finally, from a practical point of view, Carrel and Rivers succeeded in cultivating smallpox vaccine by inoculating it to cultures of cornea, skin, and embryonic tissue. The virus multiplies rapidly in the tissues of the cultures and it is probable that a chicken embryo reduced to a fine pulp can produce as much vaccine as a calf.

We have now briefly explained the method of tissue culture outside the organism. The little we have said will perhaps enable the reader to have an idea of the enormous possibilities and of the progress it represents. Thanks to Dr. Carrel, we possess an admirable tool which is capable of being further perfected and has already revealed new horizons that were unsuspected by biologists up till now.

To conform strictly to the title, this article should end here, but it may be useful to add a few lines that may not seem justified at first sight. I nevertheless deem them necessary to completely understand what are the problems of life and to evaluate our chances of resolving them some day.

Indeed, this was the goal I had in mind when writing my first article which I had considered as being part of a whole and to be followed by a second one. But in order to shape and give cohesion to this whole, it is essential to explain now why the two groups of methods which I mentioned (analysis based on physics and chemistry and purely biological methods like tissue cultures) are equally indispensable and cannot—in the actual state of our knowledge—supplement each other. Though this explanation is simple it will, nevertheless, lead us to the borders of philosophy. A philosophy to which we are led, as we shall see, by the consequences of our physical discoveries and which was certainly not foreseen by philosophers of the nineteenth century.

As shown in my preceding article, we are authorized to state the fact that every biological, physiological, and medical problem can be reduced to a series of elementary chemical and physicochemical phenomena if we take these terms in their most general meaning. Let us admit that the chemistry of proteins and of organic enzymes progress in such a way that these phenomena become familiar. The fundamental question that now arises is whether this analytical answer will satisfy us completely. In other words, *will we understand the whole biological phenomenon after having dissected it successively in its chemical and physicochemical stages?* Will we have no more questions to ask? Will the coordination between time and space seem clear to us? Will the subordination of the simultaneous and successive phenomena in the same organism—the harmony, the unity of the living being studied, no matter how simple it is—logically result from our experiments? Obviously not.

One of the gravest obstacles that we encounter—an obstacle of principle and not of detail—consists therefore in the fact that life, from the simplest to the most complex form, is the resultant of a quantity of elementary phenomena, none of which are independent and that *by isolating them, we run the risk of losing the integral phenomenon, the biological phenomenon, which is precisely the one we wanted to understand.*

Claude Bernard expressed the same idea in 1865 in the following terms: "We must recognize that determinism in life phenomena is not only a very complex determinism, but that it is at the same time a determinism that develops harmonically into a hierarchy, so that complex physiological phenomena are constituted by a series of simpler phenomena which are determined by associating and combining themselves for a final common goal."

Chemical synthesis reconstitutes what analysis had separated and gives, weight for weight, the same complex body composed of identical substances. But the problem is far more complicated when organic bodies are in question, and a considerable number of active factors are still very little known. The properties which disappear and appear in the course of analysis and synthesis are not always a simple addition or subtraction of the properties of the components. This is true even in organic chemistry where the properties of oxygen and hydrogen, for instance, do not enable us to foresee those of water which, nevertheless, results from their combination. Without even speaking of synthesis, we realize more and more that either we do not possess all the factors of the problem and that our reasoning cannot supply them, or that the physical and chemical laws that govern the material states of equilibrium are at present insufficient to completely express the biological reactions. All those who have studied living matter and elementary organisms in the laboratory by means of the most advanced physical and chemical methods and have surrounded themselves with the greatest precautions, know well that "everything happens as if life were a struggle against the physical laws," as Professor Lapicque expressed it.

How surprised Claude Bernard would have been had he been told that his successor, sixty years later, instead of having further proof of what he himself already considered assured, would, on the contrary, express himself with far more prudence. Another obstacle that arises is the result of our efforts to apply the laws of inorganic matter to phenomena which are dependent on them without, however, obeying them completely. The deviations which we observe are the measure of our ignorance.

It is not inconceivable that we shall succed in bringing all elementary biological phenomena into the framework of our exact sciences. But even if we admit this, we are faced with a dilemma. On the one hand, we know that the only methods we employ, with a few rare exceptions, are physical and chemical ones. On the other hand, we are convinced that the application of these methods, no matter how perfect, does not enable us to reach the *biological problem itself in its entirety*, but only the elements that compose it. And, if we may be allowed an imperfect but suggestive image, these elements when placed side by side do not reproduce the integral phenomenon. We ignore the plan, the coordination.

Some people are already depressed by the undeniable fact that our actual science has not yet enabled us to shed light on the most elementary phenomena of life, such as the fixation of water and its role in the tissues, for instance. But the evolution of mathematical physics has contributed in no slight measure to shake still further the optimism of the nineteenth century, by overthrowing the old ideas we were accustomed to consider as endowed with a cosmic and intangible reality.

These ideas were first undermined by the works of Gibbs and Boltzmann, which have replaced the old rigid concept of determinism by another based on the law of large numbers. This law tolerates very rare exceptions—the fluctuations—which practically escape calculation. The experimental study of elementary particles—the electron and the photon—which had remained long inaccessible and which individually seem to obey only the most disordered fantasy, has continued the work of destruction. Just recently, Heisenberg's new theory, which I cannot dwell on here, introduces a "principle of indeterminacy" in the mathematical prediction of the future and seems to deal the death blow to our old classic determinism. But we can be certain that those who will find a real difficulty in adapting themselves to the new ideas, those who will fight them with tenacity, are mystics without knowing it. They cast aside the ideas of divinity in the name of reason, but dazzled by their own brain they wasted no time in replacing it by another which they had themselves created. In the enthusiasm of this new conquest, man—drunk by facts—forgot that the links uniting these facts were his own handiwork based on postulates as undemonstrable as those from which he had enfranchised himself with so much pride.

At first science was acclaimed as a liberator. It was young, disinterested, and simple; nothing more was needed. In those days the simplicity of a theory appeared to be a proof of its value. Events have taken it upon themselves to heal us of this naive optimism of which my eminent colleague Jacques Duclaux recently said that pushed to this point it was no longer a quality.

Today we have to acknowledge that science will take a long time to keep the promises that had been made in its name. It is not science but we ourselves who are to blame, for none of the experimental facts acquired in the past has ceased to be true. Physics has never had to retract a single affirmation based on facts that were well established within accurately defined limits. The retractions that science has been forced to make do not belong to her own realm but are precisely concerned with the future. Facts remain; human anticipations vanish. The fundamental error consisted in believing that by indefinitely increasing the precision of our measurements, we would be able finally to predict the future with infinite precision. This is not the case, and beyond a certain limit we meet with the most capricious irregularities. From a practical standpoint this state of things in no way influences what we call the principle of causality which affirms that the presence of certain factors must always bring about a similar result. The law of large numbers enters into play and all our current phenomena are subject to the statistical laws which are the expression, on our scale, of an immense quantity of electronic phenomena that escape observation. Consequently, only one thing has changed: our hope in the possible mathematical prediction of the future and perhaps our ideas on the real significance of the relation between cause and effect.

THE BIOLOGICAL PROBLEM
AND THE VALUE OF THE METHODS 1931

The sciences of inorganic matter are indispensable but insufficient for the study of living matter, for neither chemistry nor physics can shed light on the harmonious coordination and subordination of vital phenomena.

It seems difficult to speak of the fundamental problems of life without first giving a definition of life itself. This is such a delicate and probably illusory task that no one would dare tackle it. However, we can attempt to give a provisional definition of a living organism, which is of more interest.

This is not as easy as it may seem, and the formula I will propose merely aims to serve as a plan. I believe, however, that it is temporarily as valid as any other, and it has the advantage of being terse and of pointing out the principal facts that should be considered. This is the formula: *A living organism is a finite and dissymmetrical portion of space-time where almost all the forces of our universe apparently act following a plan the periodic coordination of which is preestablished.*

As every word in this formula has a precise meaning, but as some of them have been employed in the accepted sense given by physical mathematics, it may be useful to study them briefly.

"Finite portion of space-time" evidently expresses the fact that every organism is limited in space and in time. Its limits in space are what we call its shape; its limits in time are what we call its birth and death.

Its ability to displace itself on our planet is not a special characteristic. There are many examples of the displacement of inert matter under the influence of various forces. The term "dissymmetrical" is taken not only in the restricted meaning of structural asymmetry, but in the far more general sense of the asymmetry of forces—of disequilibrium. In other words, I thereby express the fact that an equilibrium, chemical for instance, never exists in a normal human being, but there is a perpetual tendency towards an equilibrium which is only definitively attained at death. This state of permanent instability is truly characteristic of life. Among others Helmholtz and Pasteur observed it, and I have developed elsewhere the consequences it entails. These consequences are still in great part hypothetical and are therefore outside the scope of this article.

Almost all the forces of our universe act unceasingly in this space thus clearly defined. Are we authorized to say "all the forces" or is it preferable to prudently admit that certain forces may be absent or practically inactive? I have thought over the matter at length and I personally believe that the more general expression can be used. Indeed, as our substance is composed, in the final analysis, of molecules and atoms themselves composed of electrons in movement, we are forced to admit that all the forces found in the inorganic universe, the electric and magnetic forces, are present in the elements which compose us. The chemical forces, which are only the properties of the superficial electrons of the atoms and gravitation—the osmotic force—are evidently active in these elements. On the other hand, we ignore the part played in an organism by the feeble force called "pressure of radiation." Certain beings are free from it, and we cannot *a priori* affirm that its action is null in those who are subject to it. There may exist other forces with a slight or invalid action of which we have little or no knowledge. That is why I avoid any generalization.

These forces therefore act incessantly. We know that certain organisms can live in a state of latent life—tardigrads, rotifers, and wheatworms: But latent life is nevertheless life, although perhaps because of the very rhythm of our own existence and of our cerebral mechanism, we can only study the active normal life of the organisms which interest us; whereas the latent state, which in appearance no longer presents the characters of life represents an exceptional problem of no immediate interest.

Up to now this definition does not contain any term that cannot be applied to certain phenomena of the inorganic world, crystals for example, as well as to the artificial cells of Leduc. Its precision, its limitation are due much more to the coexistence of all these conditions. But this observation entails an important consequence accepted by Claude Bernard *a priori*—namely that the determinism of physicochemical phenomena must apply to the mechanisms found in living beings. The consequences of this conclusion will be developed further on, and we will see how these ideas have evolved in the light of the new concepts that owe their origin to the works of Gibbs and Boltzmann.

There remains the last line:"apparently act following a plan the periodic coordination of which is preestablished." The word tendency is not pronounced, but it is implicitly contained in the sentence, for if everything occurs as if there were a plan, everything occurs also as if there were a tendency to follow this plan.

This leads us into a field that we cannot call less familiar, for it surrounds us, but which, nevertheless, actually escapes the methods of investigation that enable us to establish quantitative relations between phenomena. We see this tendency manifesting itself everywhere in the form of the tendency to persist which characterizes the species. The impression it gives is that of a universal effort towards perpetuity.

We can conceive that evolution and its factors—such as adaptation, natural selection, sudden mutations, etc., in a word the means—depend on the physical and chemical laws, but the reason for this tendency escapes us completely. Nevertheless, we cannot systematically dismiss this problem from our preoccupations for it constitutes a fact as indisputable as the very existence of matter. We are no more authorized to relegate it offhand amongst the unsolvable problems of philosophy than to so relegate gravitation, which is also only known to us by its manifestations and by the admirable but still hypothetical theory of Einstein.

It is therefore important not to neglect this tendency. If at present we can do no more than ascertain it, we must never lose sight of the fact that everything occurs as if the characteristics of the living organism that are included in the first part of our definition—characteristics that connect it closely to the inorganic universe—were only the means brought into action by nature to permit this tendency to manifest itself; or if a seemingly less finalistic formula is preferred, as if these characteristics were only a manifestation of this tendency. I should like to insist on the fact that gravitation gives us a faithful picture of this proposition and yet no one dreams of attributing to this force a characteristic that is unknowable *a priori*.

Before continuing, let us open a parenthesis on this subject, in order to try and understand, through a simple example taken from daily experience, how we can visualize such a force without having recourse to the famous and obscure entelechy of Aristotle.

Picture a louse, or any very small insect hardly a millimeter long, and try to imagine the conclusions it would come to as a result of its reactions, admitting that the mechanism of its thought were of like nature and as developed as our own. Its universe is foreign to us and the laws it can deduce from it are different. A dewdrop is a rigid, practically impenetrable hillock and the tiny insect cannot possibly free itself, should it be unluckily imprisoned in it. Superficial tension on that scale becomes an important force by comparison to its mass. Now what idea can such an insect have of the higher laws which govern its life? It will be forced to admit the existence of periodical cataclysms which influence the development of its species; but as it has an imperfect mosaical sight, it has never seen and can not possibly conceive a man and will always be incapable of establishing a direct relation between its own destruction and a gardener's broom. If, as I admitted to start with, it possesses a brain similar to ours, it thinks itself the king of creation—and if it has what we have agreed to call the scientific spirit, it will have faith only in the objects on which it can experiment directly. It cannot experiment on man, no more than the vermin of an elephant can experiment on an elephant. But it will be obliged to acknowledge the reality of a "force" that reduces it to pulp without any possible reason or excuse.

To cite Charles Guye again : "It is thescale of observation that creates the phenomenon." And a phenomenon is only the appearance taken by the laws of chance on our scale of observation. You see how the framework of our concepts, which is supplied by our senses, can influence our ideas and reasoning.

I apologize for this digression and will now turn back to the last words of my definition—"the periodic coordination of which is preestablished." This expression "periodic coordination" explains itself. We find coordination everywhere, and I have used the term "periodic" to express the fact that life only seems to proceed from life itself through an identical and repeated mechanism. "Life," said Bergson, "resembles a current which goes from germ to germ through the intermediary of a developed organism." The period, variable following the species, is measured by the time that elapses between the appearance of the germs in a same line.

We have finally—*in cauda venenum*—come to the only term the meaning of which is as precise as it is mysterious: "preestablished." I do not think that any sane man, devoid of preconceived ideas, can question the fact that all living organisms develop by following a plan. Moreover, all our hopes of arriving one day at a totally scientific medicine are based on our confidence in this plan. "The physicist and the chemist," wrote Claude Bernard, "can reject any idea of final causes in the facts they observe, but the physiologist is led to admit a harmonious and preestablished finality in organized bodies whose partial actions are all interdependent and generative of each other." Further on he adds, "The primitive essence of life is in the force of organic development." Bernard was not the dupe of such a phrase. It represents not only a conviction that is difficult to express, but the influence of an epoch when literature had not yet freed itself from romantic bombast. But these observations do not prevent him from declaring his faith in the physicochemical determinism of vital manifestations which belong to the realm of science : "Life," he says, "introduces absolutely no difference in the experimental scientific method which must be applied to the study of physiological phenomena, and in this respect the physiological sciences and the physicochemical sciences, depend on identical principles of investigation. In organic as in inorganic matter, the laws are immutable and the phenomena which are governed by these laws are bound to their condition of existence by a necessary and absolute determinism."

These lines were written in 1865. They constitute a true act of faith, or, if one prefers, a bold extrapolation, for at that time it was clearly impossible to affirm the necessary nature of an absolute determinism, based on undisputed experiments. It certainly could not be affirmed today, although the exact sciences have advanced since that period. One of the clearest benefits derived from this progress consists in the new concept of determinism which has profoundly modified the significance of our experimental laws. The physicochemical law, which we had become accustomed to consider as fatal and ineluctable, has been replaced by a statistical law which, theoretically at least, admits very rare exceptions or *fluctuations*, according to the scientific term. The absolute determinism of the physical and chemical laws has given way to a statistical determinism which is broader, although practically as rigorous. The profession of faith, which was largely sentimental at the time when Claude Bernard made it, acquires a character of greater plausibility and generality in the light of the progress of mathematical physics. But, contrary to what the great physiologist might have thought, it is not by proving the rigorousness of the determinism he brandished as the emblem of his scientific philosophy that the exact sciences have given a more probable value to his words. On the contrary, it is by opening the door to the possibility of very rare fluctuations which practically escape calculation.

To study living organisms we are thus in all honesty compelled to start from two postulates. We need not define the first for we momentarily admit that it concerns the unknowable, the coordinated effort, the plan. The second, the only one which counts for us, establishes the identity of the laws governing inorganic and organized matter. Unfortunately, the latter has the value only of an indispensable working hypothesis. Our ideas have greatly evolved in the last thirty years.

"The brilliant beginnings of organic synthesis," Jacques Duclaux recently wrote, "had raised the hope that this chasm which separates physics and chemistry from biology, could be crossed by the sole resources of organic chemistry... The oft-employed formula, according to which living organisms *obey the same laws as inert chemical compounds*, dates from this period. The idea that such a formula could have been seriously considered, makes us smile today. Pushed to such a point, optimism is no longer a quality."

This postulate is therefore rather doubtful in the present state of our chemistry and physics. And yet it is the only one that has a real practical value; it is a working tool. Two postulates is a very small number. Geometry, which is a rigorous and very simple science since neither time nor matter intervene in its reasonings, is based on one famous postulate, but the theory of relativity requires about ten.

I will now try to show what we can hope to extract from this postulate which expresses faith in our science, whereas the first expresses faith in our ignorance. Our method of analysis does not differ essentially from that of the child who wants to know why the wheels of his engine turn, or what is inside a doll. We cannot deny that this method has obtained brilliant results. But we must acknowledge that science has been less successful, when after having demolished a model furnished by nature, it has tried to reconstruct a similar one. With a false simplicity, one might almost say a hypocritical modesty, nature offers toys of a confounding complexity which it manufactures in series with remarkable regularity, precision, and facility; and by apparently simple means. She seems to say: a living being, insect, fish, reptile, bird, mammal—nothing is easier. I manufacture millions every minute. When man tries to manufacture, not a living being, but simply one of the fundamental chemical substances that compose it, a protein, he fails miserably. There is no proof that he will not succeed one day. But at present we cannot affirm it. And what is a protein by comparison with the complexity of a living organism?

Man tries to copy the objects of the universe in order to know them better. But to attain this goal he always employs processes that are different from those of nature, generally less perfect and more costly from the point of view of expense of energy. A cell of the thyroid gland manufac-

46

tures thyroxin; a cell of the suprarenal glands—adrenalin; a pigment cell—pigment; a liver cell—glycogen; and the materials used are the same. These substances are not always easily made in the laboratory, and our methods are essentially different. To explain the natural process we are forced to call upon the presence of elements of which the essence and mode of action are still rather mysterious : the catalyzers, the diastases. We are rightly filled with admiration when, by means of extremely delicate and ingenious techniques, a scientist succeeds in manufacturing in the laboratory a body similar to those which our glands normally secrete. But we all possess in our bodies numerous small laboratories which resolve the same problem constantly with no other chemical products than those produced by our daily food. The indispensable tool for the complete solution of the problem, the catalyzer, is missing. So, due to this difference between the means used, we obtain only incomplete answers which must momentarily satisfy us.

Nevertheless, we are authorized to state the fact that every biological, physiological, or medical problem can be reduced to a series of elementary chemical and physicochemical phenomena if we use these terms in their most general sense. So be it. Let us admit that the chemistry of proteins and of diastases, will make such progress that these phenomena will become familiar.

We can now ask ourselves whether this analytical answer will satisfy us completely. In other words, will we understand the whole biological phenomenon we are studying when we have dissected it in its successive chemical and physicochemical stages? Will we have no more questions to ask? Will the coordination between time and space seem clear to us? Will the subordination of the simultaneous and successive phenomena in the same organism—the harmony, the unity of the living being studied —no matter how simple it is, logically follow from our experiments? Obviously not. How could it be otherwise?

One of the principal obstacles we have to overcome therefore is the following: we try to apply the laws of unorganized matter to phenomena which are dependent on them without, however, obeying them completely.

The deviations which we observe are the measure of our ignorance. Donnan's famous equilibrium is never rigorously found on both sides of a living membrane. The osmotic pressure in a living organism does not function like a Dutrochet osmometer. The difference of pressure which exists is maintained only by the work of the living membrane, which plays a fundamental part. It is the phenomenon named *Epictesis* by Lapicque. The vital equilibria are never rigorously comparable with the physical and chemical equilibria. True equilibrium is death. Bernard had clearly perceived the difference. "We must recognize, " he said, "that the determinism of the phenomena of life is not only a very complex determinism, but is at the same time a determinism which is harmoniously formed in such a way that the complex physiological phenomena are constituted by a series of simpler phenomena that determine one another by associating or combining themselves in view of a common final goal."

Why is it that the exact sciences enjoy such a dazzling prestige? It is probably due to a blind faith in the principle of causality, in the rigid determinism of the last century, and also to our justified confidence in the precision and fidelity of the methods. It is extremely probable that if our predecessors—and many of our biological colleagues—had not had this blind faith in determinism, their faith in science as a whole would have been shaken. They would feel the ground collapsing under their feet if they were told that physics and chemistry are not rigorously subject to this antiquated determinism. How could we hope to have a satisfactory science of life if the exact sciences are themselves no longer exact?

Without going to extremes and while affirming that practically nothing is changed, we must nevertheless recognize that for a long time already theoretical physics has gradually tended to deviate from a purely deterministic basis. Heisenberg, a brilliant mathematician, formulated his "Principle of Indeterminacy" in 1927. It was generally well accepted and gave the death blow to all our old ideas and to determinism by introducing a certain degree of indeterminism, or unforeseeability of the future, as a fundamental law of the universe. This different point of view trans-

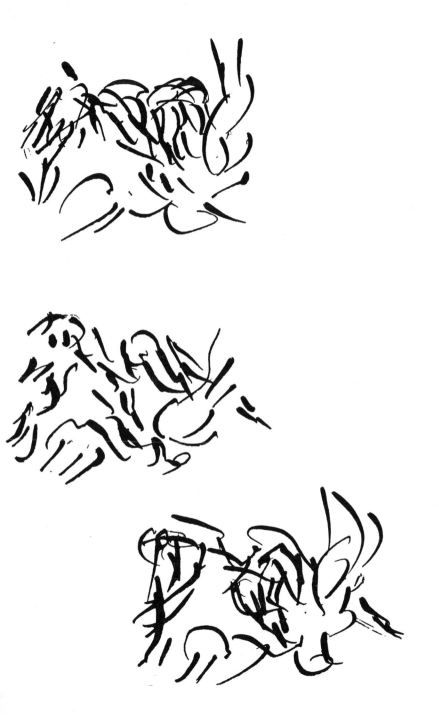

forms the flow of time into a much more tangible phenomenon than it used to be in classical physics. Every moment that passes introduces something new into the world, something that is not solely a mathematical extrapolation of all that existed previously. The classical determinism of Laplace, which dominated science for more than two centuries, stated that if complete information concerning the entire state of the universe during the first minute of the year 1600, for example, could be obtained, it would be possible to deduce all the events of the past and future by calculation.

The future would be determined by the past, just as the solution of a differential equation is determined by the limiting conditions. Heisenberg, however, demonstrated that only one half of the elements necessary to determine an event can be obtained as the other elements come into existence only after the event has taken place. It is not therefore ignorance so to speak; it is a necessary limitation. It is the principle of indeterminacy which is now fully incorporated into modern physics. My aim is not to convince you of the absolute reality of this new theory but to simply draw your attention to it, because of its great utility to undulatory mechanics—and so as to thoroughly demonstrate that even exact sciences are far from having attained their definitive form, assuming that such an expression has any meaning.

It is evident that this new concept is bound to upset the ideas of many people, especially those who unconsciously and as a result of their blind faith in Science (with a capital S) had launched themselves into farfetched extrapolations of a purely speculative and unscientific nature. The combination of sentiment and science is not often a happy one and some of the optimistic anticipations, so flattering to the human mind, may be the result of a reaction against certain moral disciplines which all tend to glorify humility and severely condemn pride. At its dawn Science was hailed as a liberator. At that time the simplicity of a theory, of a doctrine, appeared to be a proof of its value. The new discoveries and events have taken it upon themselves to cure us of this candor which, however, has not yet quite disappeared from the world.

It is easy to discover the source of the fundamental rror. The magnificent conquests of science encouraged the belief that by increasing indefinitely the precision of our measurements, we should be able to predict phenomena with ever-increasing accuracy. Unfortunately, facts have proved that this hope was illusory, for the most capricious irregularities have recently been observed when the precision of the measurements exceeds a certain point and enables us to penetrate into the hitherto inaccessible realm of the small elements; the electron and the photon. The most refined techniques do not enable us to predict the movements of these corpuscles which seem to be solely determined by the most disordered fantasy.

From a practical point of view this state of things in no way influences what we call the principle of causality which affirms that the same effect must always follow certain given factors. Indeed the law of great numbers enters into play and all our phenomena are but "envelope" phenomena and the result, on our scale, of an immense number of molecular and electronic phenomena which escape observation. Only one thing therefore is changed: our old idea of determinism, our ideas on the real significance of the relation of cause and effect.

The preceding observations can already give rise to some practical conclusions for the use of doctors, who, unlike laboratory workers, do not have the possibility of choosing and arbitrarily simplifying their problems.

The first conclusion which imposes itself is that while recognizing the interest and *necessity* of collaborating with the exact sciences for the study of biological problems, doctors must not delude themselves on the immediate usefulness of the information they can derive from it at the present time—and this for two reasons. The first is due to the ignorance which I have just pointed out and which has not yet allowed us to establish, quantitatively, the absolute identity between the phenomena of organic matter and those of inorganic matter. The second is due to the practical impossibility of making measurements under the rigorous conditions that are essential if they are to have any significance and then of interpreting the results obtained. Although the successes of chemistry and biophysics have been considerable, it must be admitted that the results in applying the data to medical problems, have not always been brilliant. Fashion takes a hand. The impression exists that certain measurements can replace experience and reasoning. Reasoning can never be replaced. The pH, the isoelectric point, viscosity, the refractive index, etc., are precious tools for a small number of researchers who are richly endowed and can dispose of all their time. But they can, however, become dangerous weapons in the hands of the majority by distorting the diagnostic through the fallacious security given by a precision which is often illusory.

We must not forget that these measurements do not possess a great significance when they are considered by themselves, for we are forced by our ignorance to neglect a hundred other factors which play an equally important part. Moreover, there is nothing to prove that all these integral forces which represent on our scale quantities of elementary phenomena of a molecular and atomic order, play a role of their own. We have only to think a moment to realize that most of the forces we know how to measure can vary only within very narrow limits, and that one or several complicated mechanisms exist for each of them whose purpose seems to be to maintain them within these limits. The word "buffer" has been used to define the mechanism which maintains the concentration of hydrogen ions, constant. But this same word could apply to numerous other phenomena—to all the regulating systems in general. In the blood there is a "buffer" mechanism, which regulates excessive variations of superficial tension. It is the adsorbent power of the proteins. For the variations of blood pressure these are the vasodilator and vasoconstrictor mechanisms which bring the suprarenal glands and the secretion of adrenalin into play when needed. Thus, when we ascertain experimentally that one of the important elements of the normal equilibrium of tissue fluids has varied excessively, it is impossible to decide in the majority of cases whether the deviation is due to a disturbance of the fundamental function or to a disturbance of the regulating mechanisms. It must be noted that the result is the same from our point of view; we conclude that there has been an accident. But we had already been informed of this by clinical observations, and we must admit that a confirmation with two decimals, generally devoid of significance, does not help us much as yet.

I do not wish the foregoing words to be wrongly interpreted and to lead to the conclusion that the clinical laboratory is useless. On the contrary, I am convinced that it is indispensable, especially when techniques that have not been fully developed are not prematurely applied. But I am even more convinced that it will be much more indispensable twenty or fifty years hence, when the sustained efforts of the laboratories of physiology and general biology, working in close cooperation with those of physics and chemistry, will have shed some light on the fundamental problems of life.

We must confess that we have not yet reached the stage when laboratory measurements, no matter how excellent, can replace the clinical sense.

Widal did not make this mistake, but the same cannot be said of certain foreign schools. To illustrate our ignorance I will cite some examples of simple biological problems that are actually still very mysterious. Let us take an elementary fact; the role of water in the tissues. All tissues contain a certain proportion of water, which seems fixed in such a way that it cannot be eliminated without entailing death. A muscle, which is about as hydrated as gelatine gel with 80 percent of water does not give out a drop of water when submitted to a very strong pressure. When water appears, after a certain time of compression, it means that the muscle is dead—it no longer contracts.

An earth worm can be desiccated until it has lost 43 % of the water it contains. It is then fragile and brittle, like dry clay. When replaced in water it comes back to life. But if the desiccation is pushed to 50 %—which does not represent a very big difference—the worm can never again be resuscitated. What idea can we have of the mode of fixation of this water and of the role it plays in these two cases? None at all. A jelly fish contains about one thousandth part of solid matter. Nine hundred and ninety-nine parts of its weight are represented by water. Can it be said that life and all the functions of the jelly fish are entirely localized in that infinitesimal, one thousandth part of its substance? This is in all likelihood false, whereas it can in all probability be maintained that life is a consequence of the combination of solid substances and water, of whatever nature it is. It is impossible to state that the heart is more necessary than the liver or the kidneys in the human body. Life from the simplest to the most complex is the resultant effect of a quantity of elementary phenomena, none of which are independent, and if we consider them separately, we run the risk of losing sight of the integral phenomenon—the biological phenomenon, the one we particularly wanted to understand.

We intentionally chose very simple examples. It can be readily understood that they become more striking the higher up one goes in the scale of living beings and when they are studied in relation to their environment. But it is rash, to say the least, to concentrate solely on the study of the proteins of the organism in order to establish the laws which govern a living cell; or on the study of isolated cells, in order to understand the economy, the subordination, and the harmony of a whole organism. We cannot hope to solve all the biological problems concerning an individual by isolating him and removing him from the influence of numerous unknown factors which contribute in different degrees to creating and maintaining these normal conditions of evolution. This principle applies to cells that are surrounded by other cells endowed with different properties and influenced not only by those with whom they are in contact, but by other very distant cells by means of the nervous system. It applies to endocrine glands, to complete organs, and simple mechanisms that are perpetually active and all more or less directly joined to each other by links that are more or less rigid and in a state of permanent instability. It applies to the entire organism, first in relation to its material surroundings, its medium, and also in relation to the other living organisms which surround it, be they harmful or beneficial. It is important to study the parasites of ants if we wish to have a perfect knowledge of ants. The metabolism of certain animals depends on the reasons which impel the smaller animals they feed on to emigrate periodically. How many purely biological enigmas are encountered in the physiology of termites and of insects in general? At present it is difficult to conceive the combination of laws and of physicochemical facts which will give a completely satisfactory explanation of the anatomy and physiology of those which are incapable of nourishing themselves and depend entirely on their co-workers, or of the phenomena known by the name of "conditional reflexes."

We need only to read Fabre and the great writer Maeterlinck to be convinced that the study of insects reveals thousands of baffling problems. But the behavior of more evolved beings is no less strange. How can we explain the fact that eels leave the soft waters of their rivers once a year, cross the seas, cover thousands of miles, and mate in a pit of the Saragossa Sea? There may be other analogous centers in the Pacific Ocean. There they spawn. The eggs hatch in this salt medium and when the little eels have grown, they travel the same distance in the opposite direction and return to populate our rivers. How many times are we tempted to ask "why?" This "why" includes the "how" and something else besides which seems very important and is, perhaps, not included in the "how." This is the important biological problem.

In the examples cited I have purposely left aside the still more complex phenomena of human pathology and the normal and abnormal phenomena that depend more directly on the nervous system. It is very evident that in the cases where the influence of the brain on the organism is concerned we are completely out of our depth. It is still a world of mystery and we can only say that it is as vast as our ignorance on the subject. The part played by the nervous system in man is considerable, and we are unfortunately obliged to neglect it completely in order to study the physicochemistry of biological phenomena. The systematic elimination of this factor is sufficient to explain many failures.

Apparently we are now faced with a dilemma. On the one hand, we know that the only methods we have to attack the fundamental elementary problems of biology—taken in the widest and most extended sense—are the physical and chemical methods. On the other hand, we are convinced that the application of these methods, no matter how perfect, does not enable us to reach the biological problem itself as a whole, but only the elements that compose it. Now these elements, if we may use an imperfect but evocative image, when placed side by side do not reproduce the integral phenomenon. We ignore the plan—the coordination.

On the one hand, we have precise methods, elaborated for the study of simple phenomena, with a limited number of variables which we manage to apply, after a fashion, to certain vital phenomena. On the other hand, we have an infinite number of problems that are rather vaguely acknowledged, but nevertheless fundamental, and we do not have as yet any well-defined method for studying them.

I see therefore only two possible roads towards knowledge : the first is direct and consists in affirming *a priori* that the methodical application

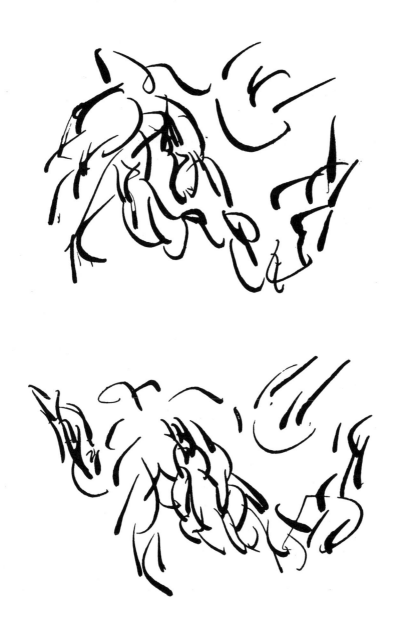

of techniques and disciplines elaborated for the study of inert matter must forcibly lead us to the comprehension of living matter and to the knowledge of the correlation of phenomena. The point of departure is a postulate which can be called the mechanistic postulate, entirely subjective—sentimental one might say—as it rests only on a very probable but not demonstrable conviction; in brief, *a credo*. The second path which is open to us consists, on the contrary, in not resting on an act of faith but in working by employing all possible methods and in hoping that the intelligent study of life itself will allow us to find a short cut and bring us closer to our goal in one quick spurt. A marvelous example of this way of thinking and acting was given us by Pasteur. Human genius is in itself an infinitely superior tool to the tools it manufactures. It must remain the master, and we must be vigilant so as to keep it from becoming enslaved by disciplines issued from itself but whose value is momentary. Without postulating anything except that the intelligence of man will persist and that no social revolution will keep it from acting freely and developing, this road is assuredly the most scientific and, above all, the most reasonable. The only real criterion, said Claude Bernard, is reason. Let us avoid being systematic. Blind belief in the fact that pretends to silence reason is as dangerous for the experimental sciences as sentimental beliefs, which also silence reason.

What conclusions can we draw from the preceding lines? I think the most important is the following one. It is the biologist who finds himself in direct contact with living matter, whatever his specialty, and who has to state the problem to the physicist and chemist. But the possibility of an answer depends on the way the questions are phrased. They must not be put lightly and without having been well defined beforehand. The biologist must follow step by step the progress of the physicochemical experiments, without ever losing sight of the global biological problem, that is to say, the same problem considered as part of a whole, as an element in a whole. Theoretically, only the biologist is capable of embracing the harmony of the edifice. Let him not forget it. Let him not be blinded by the importance of the immediate practical problem. He must lift himself above the daily routine by an effort of will and intelligence and not let himself be overwhelmed by the small details that overshadow the main theme. His vision must be lofty and wide. Every phenomenon, no matter how small, contains a part of the majesty derived from its subordination to the whole. Man has created the artificial notion of independent variables for the needs of the cause. There are no independent variables in nature. Everything is bound together; everything is linked. It is by being convinced of the grandeur of his role that the modern biologist will contribute gradually to dispelling the profound darkness which surrounds man and in which his brain flounders in a secular combat, of which the social convulsions themselves are perhaps only an echo.

AGEING 1933

The title of this chapter might suggest that we intend to study ageing in its outward manifestations or the chances we have of slowing the flight of "inexorable" time or of repairing its "irreparable ravages." This is not the case. By basing ourselves on experimental facts we simply intend to explain the fundamental difference that exists between absolute or conceptual time—the physical, sidereal time—and physiological time. Only physiological time counts from the point of view of our ageing. It is not identical with the others but on the contrary displays very different characteristics.

The problem of the reality of the external world has always preoccupied philosophers. Struck by the fact that our knowledge of the universe rests, in the last analysis, on the accumulation of our preceding sense impressions, of our thoughts, and of our memories, they asked themselves what relation there was between the world conceived as an "ejection," a projection of our sensorial and psychological experience outside of ourselves, and the real universe such as it is *in itself*. Some of the most celebrated thinkers, profoundly impressed by the primordial role of the human brain, have even completely denied the existence of anything outside of ourselves. The majority agree in admitting that the notion of a "thing in itself" is futile. If the monad of Leibnitz represents the extreme limit of the anthropocentric concept of the universe, we must admit that the other theories have only added "windows on the exterior" without shedding any light on the nature of the source of sense impressions thus created. For us, the real world—the result of the conjunction of space and time—resides in the "construction" that we project outside of ourselves. We form concepts and draw inferences from the impressions of our senses by mental association. These are the facts of science whose domain is essentially formed by the contents of our brain.

Space and time have long ago ceased to be considered as realities of the world of phenomena; they are modes which enable us to perceive things separately. They can be neither infinitely extended nor indefinitely divided. They are essentially limited by the contents of our perception. Entire volumes have been written on the subject, and any bachelor of letters or philosophy remembers these questions more or less vaguely. Lacking direct experimental data, they still belong to the realm of pure philosophy. Nevertheless, as Carrel pointed out, a difference exists between the physical, sidereal time measured by our clocks, based on observations manifestly external to ourselves, and our human duration which as much as the space in which we evolve is a constituent part of our physiological and psychological self. According to Bergson the states of consciousness are so many instantaneous pictures which detach themselves on a background animated by a uniform speed. But our *duration* depends on our organism as a whole: mind and body are two aspects of the same thing and determined as much by our structural and functional states as by our psychic states. The time in which we live includes physiological time as well as psychological time. We measure it in years, days, and hours, which flow in uniform fashion, inexorably, following the movements of the planets. This conventional measurement obviously struck our intelligence as being the simplest, but it postulates the identity of physical time and of physiological duration. This postulate is useful if not legitimate. On what is it based?

Even to a superficial observer internal physiological time does not seem to flow at a constant rate within the frame of external time. Everyone knows that real age can differ from legal age. The value of a day is not identical for ephemeral insects and for animals that live to be a hundred years old. Even for one individual this value seems to vary for do we not rightly say that for man "time passes more quickly in maturity and in old age than during childhood"? Our *duration* would therefore be independent to a certain degree of sidereal time. If the movements of the planets and of the clocks were slowed or accelerated simultaneously it might be possible, although we cannot be certain of it, that physiological time would not be affected by it. Each human being constitutes a relatively independent universe in a state of continuous transformation. It is the rate of this transformation which can be considered as characteristic of our specific duration; of our physiological time.

The few preceding lines may have sufficed to show how interesting it would be to measure this physiological time *directly* without bringing in an external standard whose relation to our duration if not completely independent, yet escapes our immediate observation. It can readily be seen that such a measurement is connected to the philosophical problem we evoked at the beginning of this chapter: the reality of the external world. So far we have been obliged to borrow from intersidereal space the frame in which our self evolves; the network of our duration. We have thus based ourselves involuntarily on a philosophical opinion: our faith in the reality of this universe. But even more serious is the fact that we have confused two different things: time and duration.

We will now try to show how we can free ourselves from the postulate on which the measurement of physiological duration has rested until now, and how we can reverse the problem, namely express sidereal time in units of physiological time; in other words, compare the evolution in time of the external world to a standard drawn from within ourselves and therefore of unquestionable reality.

Newton when defining "conceptual" time expresses himself thus: "That absolute, true, and mathematical time is conceived as flowing at a constant rate, unaffected by the acceleration or retardation of the motions of material things."

Clearly, such a time is a pure ideal without practical significance, for how can we measure it if there be nothing in the sphere of our perception which we are certain flows at a constant rate? The movement of the earth around the sun and of the earth around its axis or, if one prefers, the sensations determined in us by these phenomena—sensations that we project outside of ourselves—seem to show evidence of complete regularity. By admitting that the speed of the earth on its course is constant between two points, we divide the distance traveled in equal quantities which must be covered in equal times, and we thus create the subdivisions of our units of time; the year for example. These subdivisions are again broken up into smaller units and so on. We have created perfected mechanisms (clocks, chronometers) which are regulated according to the movements of our planet and enable us by means of their hands to follow with the eye and with the greatest precision what we call the uniform flow of time.

We can also measure this time by observing other periodic phenomena; light for instance. Without being aware of it all of us have employed other less precise but picturesque units and evaluated time by referring to a distance traveled or to a work accomplished. We often employ expressions such as: the time to dress, the time to go to the post office and back, the time to count to a hundred. In piece work this is replaced by the number of pieces manufactured and in the country the area mowed by a trained laborer working regularly enables him to estimate his work hours. Supposing he cuts on an average two hundred and fifty square yards an hour. If he has worked four hours ,we know that he has cut a thousand square yards. On the other hand, if we do not know how long he has worked but can measure the surface mowed, two thousand square yards for example, we will conclude that he has worked eight hours.

All these times are arbitrary and relative. If, as we stated above, the movements of the earth and planets underwent a slight slowing down or acceleration in the course of centuries, we could only observe it by means of our astronomical clocks. But how can we be sure that the error does not stem from a variation in the gravitational field of the earth which would have affected all the pendulums of our clocks, thereby increasing or decreasing the value of the second? The time registered by our clocks expresses the fractions of time registered by the planets. Therefore we could never be sure that our instruments were right. We possess no absolute, invariable unit of time. Neither does the seemingly constant speed of light enable us to resolve the question, for if two observers, separated by a thousand years, obtain different figures what can they conclude with certitude? That the speed of light has really varied or that the difference comes from their way of measuring time?

Following the example given by Einstein: if we are in a train which is moving parallel to another and in the same direction, we cannot tell the absolute rate of speed of that train even if we are certain that ours is moving at a constant rate. We can at best only obtain the ratio of our two rates, a ratio independent of the absolute speed, for if the two trains are slowed or accelerated in the same proportion we will not be aware of it.

Physiological time, on the other hand, is very different. As the animal grows and develops in space it evolves in time, but each moment that passes, far from disappearing without leaving a trace, on the contrary, persists in the present and accumulates and contributes in creating the history of the individual. It takes a certain time for an organism to attain its full development and every day and every hour introduces physical, chemical, and psychological changes which are at the base of all the subsequent changes. Sidereal time flows at a constant speed like an endless belt mounted on two pulleys with equidistant points that pass in front of our eyes. Physiological time, on the contrary, has a beginning and an end. We will shortly demonstrate that this is not the only difference, but that furthermore its rate of flow is not constant between these two extreme limits.

We have already pointed out that, *a priori*, the same intervals of sidereal time which are by definition identical to each other, do not seem to correspond to identical values in the organized world. This is not only a fact of observation but an experimental fact. It is possible to modify the duration and the rate of life of certain cold-blooded animals as Jacques Loeb demonstrated by breeding small flies which evolved, attained adult age, and then died in twenty days, forty days, three months or six months following the temperature at which they were maintained. A decrease of ten degrees in the temperature corresponded to an increase to approximately twice the duration of life. On the other hand, in his admirable experiments on tissue cultures outside of the organism, Carrel demonstrated that it was possible to obtain fragments of living tissue, colonies of cells, in full reproductive activity subject to neither old age nor death. For more than twenty years, thus surpassing by far the maximum duration of the life of the animal from which they were extracted, they proliferated at the same rate when the toxic products they engender were eliminated every two days. The manifestations of old age in those elementary systems are therefore the result of the normal accumulation of poisons, for if they are eliminated as fast as they are produced, old age, i.e. the decrease of physiological activity, does not take place.

How can we measure age, the *real* ageing of an organism, without having recourse to physical time, this standard of measurement which is external to us, the time of our clocks?

This can be accomplished by two different methods: the method of tissue culture and the method based on the study of the cicatrization of wounds.

The first, established by Carrel, rests on the following fundamental experiments. When small fragments of living tissue are extracted from an animal and placed in a medium containing practically no nutritive substances, they manifest a certain growth activity and increase in volume during a few days. The duration and speed of this phenomenon, which express the residual growth energy of the tissues, can be easily measured. This energy is greater in an embryo than in a newborn animal. It decreases still further during youth and adult age. The ageing of an organism cannot be followed up to an advanced age by means of this method as the differences between the growth energy of adult and aged animal tissue are too slight to be estimated with precision. Furthermore, each type of tissue, every species of cell, seems to register time in its own way. But

these modifications of the growth energy of the tissues as a function of age are evidently linked to mutually related and simultaneous variations in the body fluids, in the blood for example. The tissues and organs that bathe in interstitial liquids and blood plasma constitute, in short, a rather isolated world where every local change reverberates throughout the whole. The growth energy of the tissues by decreasing with age reflects parallel modifications in the functional state and the chemical structure of plasma. These modifications are irreversible, increase during the whole life, and are measurable as Carrel brilliantly demonstrated.

Indeed, he found that under certain conditions blood serum (the liquid part of the blood, divested of its fibrin and its white and red globulae) slowed the growth of pure conjunctive cell cultures taken from a chick embryo and known by the name of "fibroblasts." The ratio of the surface of a colony of fibroblasts in serum to the surface of a colony of sister cells in a solution deprived of a serum, was named the *growth index of serum*. The smaller this "growth index" is the greater the inhibitive action, or if one prefers, the toxic power of the serum. Now the serum of a newborn dog, for example, has no inhibitive action on the cultures; the speed of growth is the same in the experiment as in the witness deprived of serum. The growth index equals 1. But serum taken from slightly older dogs soon begins to slow the cellular increase. The "growth index" decreases very rapidly during the first months of life, more slowly during youth, and generally attains a low value at a mature age. This means that the dog serum has become very toxic for the cultures. When the animal approaches old age the variations in the value of the index are so slight that they can hardly be measured.

Although this method entails experimental difficulties and does not tend itself to great precision, it has brought out the irreversible alterations that appear in the blood when the animal ages and has demonstrated that these phenomena were produced very rapidly at the beginning of life and were afterwards slowed to attain an almost constant value in old age.

The second method [1] based on the cicatrization of wounds, which we studied at the front during the war at Field Hospital No. 21, leads to exactly the same result. It rests on the following facts.

If the outline of a surface wound is carefully traced on a sterile sheet of cellophane and the area thus delimited is evaluated in square centimeters, the progress of cicatrization can be followed day by day. By subtracting successively the surface measured from one obtained previously, it was found that the difference expressed in the surface cicatrized daily is not constant but decreases in proportion as the wound itself decreases. If the points representing the successive surfaces are carried on millimeter paper where the ordinates (vertical scale) represent the areas in square centimeters and the abscissae (horizontal scale) the time in days, it can be seen that for a normal sterile wound these points can be united by a regular curve of geometrical progression.

The discovery of the algebraic equation of this curve, namely the mathematical law of cicatrization which enables one to calculate in advance the date of the total cicatrization and the successive dimensions of the wound, is of evident interest. Our ignorance of the factors that intervene in this phenomenon raised difficulties, but the discovery of these factors was to give us precious information on the mechanisms of cicatrization. We finally found that the surface of the wound and the age of the man gave all the elements needed to calculate the whole curve by means of a fairly simple formula. In other words, by knowing *the age of the wounded man and the surface of the wound* it was possible to foresee the date of healing.

From that moment on we could not only foretell the date on which every wounded man could be discharged but also the theoretical normal surface of the wound at every intermediate stage. By normal surface we mean the surface of a wound maintained in the best conditions, with an ideal dressing that prevents infection without irritating the tissues,

1. Which was chronologically the first, but which we have placed in second place because of the developments it attained.

in other words that allows nature to act for the best. The main interest resided in the possibility thus obtained of detecting the appearance of retarding factors and recognizing the relative importance of infection, irritation, movement, etc. In particular, this method made it possible to try out a great number of antiseptics and so-called cicatrizing dressings in a few days and to establish indisputably that no substance or product capable of accelerating the cicatrization of a sterile wound existed. This covers the practical side of the formula which demonstrated the supremacy of the so-called Carrel-Dakin method.

There was one coefficient in this formula, the *index of cicatrization* designated by the symbol *i*, which depended both on the age of the patient and the area of the wound. From a scientific point of view the discovery of this index of cicatrization had a deeper interest. Indeed, it made it possible for the first time *to measure the flow of physiological time*, as Carrel pointed out. There is a remarkable similarity between the index of cicatrization and Carrel's growth index. They have the same aspect as a function of age; both are important at the start of life and decrease quickly at first, then slowly attain a very low value at maturity and at the beginning of old age. Nevertheless, as we stated above, the index *i* remained a function of the area of the wound, and therefore did not have the character of universality necessary to express the age, and *solely* the age. We therefore renewed our calculations and finally obtained a new coefficient designated as the *physiological constant of reparation* by means of the symbol A, which is absolutely independent of the area and which depends only on the age. It is impossible to affirm that this constant applies to other physiological processes. But its importance is nevertheless real for, as we have already stated, the rate of reparation is parallel to the rate of growth defined by Carrel and expresses a state of equilibrium of the whole organism which corresponds to its stage of true ageing.

It is remarkable that Carrel's growth index which is based on the evolution of simple systems, of groups of cells artificially separated from the organism itself, has an aspect identical to that of the curve of the index of cicatrization or of the constant A, considering that the relations be-

tween the tissues, the organs and the "internal medium" as Bernard said—lymph and blood—are infinitely more complex in superior animals and in man. These liquids, though continually modified by products resulting from the metabolism, nevertheless retain an almost invariable composition thanks to the work of the lungs, the kidneys, the liver, and so on. And yet, in spite of all these regulating mechanisms, the plasma, and through its influence the tissues, are gradually modified. It is evident that to really control the results of certain cures or operations of so-called rejuvenation, one of the two methods we have just described would have to be employed. Unfortunately no one tries to be rejuvenated unless he is really old, and at an advanced age the differences in the index are too small to be precise. At any rate, the process of ageing is irreversible and any rejuvenation can only be artificial and momentary.

The value of the figures obtained through the study of the cicatrization of wounds derives on the one hand from the fact that they are based on a great number of cases, and on the other hand that all the men wounded in war shared practically identical conditions and were generally in excellent physical health. Outside of the principal retarding cause, bacterial infection, there are certain pathological states that influence the rate of cicatrization: diabetes, for example. But every time an obser-

ved experimental curve deviated from the calculated curve one could be certain that if the wound was bacteriologically sterile, the man was ill or else that his *real physiological age did not correspond to his legal civic age*. Some of the wounded men we treated were thirty years old but their rate of cicatrization was that of a man of forty. In other words, we obtained a true estimation of the real ageing of the organism based on the divergence observed between the age in years and the age calculated from the measured rate of reparation. Indeed, if we can know the age of the man and the area of the wound by calculating the time that a wound will take to cicatrize, reciprocally if we know the total time, or else the speed of cicatrization and the area of the wound, we can calculate the index; that is to say find the age corresponding to that rate. In 80 % of the cases the calculation agreed with the experiment. But depending on the ancestral heritage, the conditions of existence, the excesses, the privations or the hardships undergone during life, a certain number of individuals age more quickly than others.

The majority of men between twenty and forty years old who live in the country lead a hard but healthy life. It was their rate of reparation which was considered as normal and which was compared to the rate of reparation of the others. It is therefore the real age which is measured, the degree of ageing, by means of a unit of physiological time of the same nature, instead of having to depend on a physical unit which is external to us: the number of revolutions that the world has made around the sun; i.e., the years. Unexpectedly, the preciseness of the formula was such that the total deviation of cicatrization could be calculated within a day or two, even for wounds which required three months or more to heal. The difference between the observed and calculated intermediate areas hardly exceeded one square centimeter for wounds of forty or fifty square centimeters, which represents an error of the order of two or three percent. The preciseness of the measurement of the area itself was not generally within this figure, which indicates that the difference between the experiment and the calculation could be due to an imperfect method for evaluating the area.

The value of the decreases in physiological activity between childhood and adult age, or if one prefers, of the decrease of the constant A, can be shown by the following example: if a healthy man who is twenty years old cicatrizes 10 square centimeters of a wound in ten days, he will require 13 days at thirty, 18 days at forty, 25 days at fifty and 32 days at sixty-five to cicatrize the same area. A child of ten will take only about six and a half days.

Now, when a wound cicatrizes, what does it do? It accomplishes a *piece of work*. Just as a mason closes up a breach in a wall, nature repairs a breach in our organism. When we measure the velocity at which this work is accomplished by means of physical sidereal time, we observe that it is very great at the beginning of life, slower at the middle and slower still at the end. If the number 100 represents the velocity at the age of twenty, it will only be 55 at thirty and 31 at sixty. But it is expressed by 155 at the age of ten. *It is, therefore, not constant with respect to our unit of measurement.* At different ages, it takes different lengths of time to accomplish the same amount of work: the cicatrization of one square centimeter of a wound. If we reason in the same way as in the case of the reaper we can utilize this work to estimate the sidereal time, that is to say *we can measure the physical time in units of physiological time.*

Seeing that this physiological time is truly our own, our "internal" time, and that humoral reactions and vital phenomena as a whole are governed by it more than by the rhythm of the earth's rotation ("external" time), this comparison can be interesting.

When we refer to *sidereal* time as being the canvas on which the pattern of our existence is spread, we notice that the time needed to accomplish a certain unit of physiological work of repair is about four times greater at fifty than at ten years of age. *Everything therefore occurs as if sidereal time flows four times faster for a man of fifty than for a child of ten.* From the point of view of the internal self many more things happen in a sidereal year for a child than for an old man. The year therefore seems to flow more slowly and the figures we have established—the constant A—enable us to realize not only by how much our physiological activity decreases but also *by how much physical time is accelerated in respect to ourselves.*

Thus when we take physiological time as a unit of comparison, we find that physical time no longer flows uniformly. Physiologically, one year is much longer for a child than for its parents. Supposing the parents are forty years old and the child is ten; one year for the latter represents about three years for the first. If the child is younger, the difference is still greater, but we lack experimental figures to calculate it. We are only authorized to employ a calculating method known as extrapolation, which does not offer the same guarantees of security. As an indication we can, however, state that it is probable that between the ages of one and five, one year equals from seven to twelve years for a man of forty.

Therefore, young and old united in the same space live in separate universes where the value of time is radically different. Neither pedagogues nor psychologists seem as yet to have taken into account the considerable importance of this unequal value at the different stages of life. The manner in which this could be done is by no means evident. But this is another problem.

As Carrel points out, it is certain that though these divergences are only clearly established for physiological time, they also constitute one of the elements of our consciousness; of our psychological perception of time. Though we can discuss the fact that our perception is entirely conditioned by the same chemical and physicochemical phenomena that are at the base of our physiological ageing, we can hardly deny that it is related to it in some way. To explain the apparently much more rapid flight of time as we grow older by invoking memory alone is an insufficient hypothesis, for it does not take into account the profound perturbations which must reverberate on all the functions of the organism and which are measured by the constant of the rate of reparation. The amplitude of the phenomena may not be the same everywhere, the coefficient may vary for different functions, but it cannot be eliminated. And, moreover, what is memory, and how does it function?

Whatever the answer, such a discussion is vain at the present stage of our knowledge or, to use a more significant term, of our ignorance. The important and indisputable fact is that physiological time does not have the same value at the start of life as at its decline, and that in respect to ourselves, everything takes place as if its flow were four times faster at the age of fifty than at ten.

This entails some more general observations. This physiological time can only exist for organisms capable of being born, of ageing, and of dying normally. This word "normally" contains in substance the greater part of the unsolved problems of biology, taken in its broadest sense. It implies, for instance, the action of the organic regulating mechanisms which express the fundamental difference between the healthy normal growth of cells and the abnormal anarchical growth of cancerous cells. Between a malignant tumor on the one hand, and a healing wound, which cicatrizes by rapid cellular proliferation set off in a healthy tissue by the wound itself, there is—barring the morphological difference of the cells—the following difference only: proliferation stops instantaneously when reparation is ended in healthy tissue, whereas the growth of cancerous tissue ignores this regulating mechanism and continues to proliferate until death. It suffices to wound healthy cells, to bring about a break of continuity in our skin, for all the adjacent cells, which were practically

75

inactive until then to begin to multiply: but as soon as the injury is repaired the cells revert to their former state, cease to divide and return to their normal specific physiological activity. In cancer, on the contrary, once the impetus has been given, nothing can stop it any more.

A similar phenomenon takes place when tissue cultures are washed every two days and then cut in two and replaced in a new drop of the nutritive medium; these cells, which proliferate very slowly in the organism, are seized by a frenzy of growth and reproduce with great rapidity. A culture of two square millimeters doubles its volume in 48 hours indefatigably—one can even say indefinitely. The elimination of the toxic waste products of nutrition suppresses ageing in this fragment of tisssue, and just as for the cancer cells, physiological time ceases to exist or rather is blended into sidereal time. Every individual cell, in the culture as well as in the tumor, is born, ages, and is divided or dies. Each one undergoes an evolution which is probably subject to physiological time, but the tumor, or the culture as a whole, grows at a rate that no longer reflects the age of the organism and ignores physiological time.

In conclusion it may be useful to clear up a misunderstanding arising from a phrase which though correct in itself often gives rise to an alluring but inaccurate interpretation. This phrase is the following: The average span of human life has been prolonged by several years, during the last century. The word "average" implies the presence of a large number of men, several millions, who instead of dying on an average at fifty today attain the age of sixty. If the number of sexagenarians in ratio to a given population increases, we will say that there is an increase in the average duration of human existence. It simply signifies that nowadays a child has more chance of attaining the age of sixty than it did in the past. In other words, like white bread or a car, old age has been put within reach of a greater number of individuals. But those who had the possibility of ageing do not live any longer; the extreme limit of old age has probably not been pushed back for several centuries. The mere fact that there are more sexagenarians naturally results in there being more septuagenarians and octogenarians: the law of probabilities enters into play. However, it is impossible to affirm that there is a real increase in supplementary years if the factor "chance" thus introduced is eliminated. We do not know how to prolong the duration of a human organism any more than we know how to accelerate the rate of cicatrization of a wound beyond the limit imposed by the physiological activity corresponding to a given age.

Moreover, even if it were admitted that several years of existence could be gained—which is doubtful—they would only be "sidereal" years

and their value expressed in physiological units would correspond to a very much smaller number. These years of old age, added at the end of our existence, would in no way affect the state of ageing characteristic of our true age which is solely determined by the physiological time elapsed since birth. We would like to believe that if we had ten more years to live this would be equivalent to a rejuvenation of ten years. Such is not the case. The extra years, which are only worth a fraction of the years of our youth, would prolong us such as we are and if certain methods enable us to obtain a recrudescence of activity, it is very probable that no matter how appreciable it is, we only acquire it at the detriment of our total duration.

Behind the severity of the phrases, behind the uncompromising words that I have been forced to employ to assure precision of thought, trying at the same time to avoid odious pedantry, behind the complexity of the experiments, the reader can perhaps discern the curve representing the trend of human destiny. A denuded tree seen through a muslin curtain can seem either sharply outlined or blurred in the distance, depending on whether our eyes are riveted on the branches or on the transparent material. Likewise, our fate can seem tragic when we see only its inexorable brutality, or tolerable and even pleasing when we see it through a veil. The result is about the same, whether this veil is a light gauze that softens the clearness of the lines and keeps us from seeing their extreme limits, or a net that divides the landscape into a multitude of small pictures. It is in this that the artist resembles the scientist. Our personality—that powerful and mysterious reality—determines the size of the mesh. The mesh of the artist is so fine that the details escape him in the beauty of the whole; that of the scientist, on the contrary, brings into prominence the details it frames and on which his entire thought is concentrated. Some men are wise enough not to train their eyes on the landscape beyond and are content to see it through their own personnality. They are happiest, for ageing is progressive, and in a healthy being the regulating mechanisms, mentioned above usually adjust the appetites in accordance with the means of satisfying them. Our great injustice towards ageing comes from our memory of past joys and from the desire, seemingly excused by our civilization, to revel in the same pleasures beyond their normal term of duration. Old age is not terrible if we consider it as a source of new experiences and not as the death of youth and a farewell to the past.

THE LABORATORY AND SCIENTIFIC RESEARCH
1939

The laboratory... I cannot write this word without emotion. For me, as for all my colleagues, it evokes so many memories, so many events, emotions, hopes. The laboratory is not only the setting of our material life, the place where a great part of our existence has been spent, but is above all, the nucleus of our intellectual life and even, at times, of our sentimental life. The writer, the artist, the philosopher work wherever they happen to be and borrow their inspiration from the whole universe. To produce, the scientist needs "the serene peace of the laboratories and the libraries," following Pasteur's beautiful phrase. He is only happy there. It is the quiet haven, the port of still waters, where smooth, concentric ripples are the only witness of external convulsions and sterile disorder.

I have already written three times on the sciences of life in general; on modern methods and a special method: the culture of tissues outside the organism, and on the philosophical consequences that could be drawn from the application of methods of measurement and calculus to a biological problem—ageing. But I have not yet dwelt on the laboratory itself, the "location designed for carrying out chemical, pharmaceutical and biological experiments," as Littré defined it.

Is it not striking, moreover, that it is the only place where people work which derives its name from the latin word *laborare*—to work? Yet people work everywhere; in shops, offices, outdoors, and in the mines. But these are secondary labors, and the two principal French words derived from *laborare* are *labourer* (ploughing) and *laboratoire* (laboratory). Thus are coupled a fundamental symbolic manual work, which assures existence, with intellectual creative work resulting from the impact of our intelligence with the perceptible universe, which has determined and then affirmed the supremacy of man and has given him the world for a kingdom. I hasten to add that the term "secondary" which I used to characterize all other human efforts, should not be taken as a classification in order of merit. This would be absurd. The word "secondary" simply indicates an order of appearance and dependence, as the origin of the laboratory can be traced back to the epoch when men, still covered with animal skins, discovered the power of fire. The first laboratories were apparently the caves and huts where minerals were passed through fire to obtain iron, tin, and copper. The first chemists made the first alloys: bronze and fused glass. There was no differentiation between the laboratory and the factory for thousands of years, but the problems became more complicated, knowledge increased, and as a result, the two activities became separated. However, in spite of the immense progress realized by modern techniques, we remain dumbfounded by the intelligence, the ability, and the knowledge of our ancestors. Glassware, colored enamels, perfumes, dyes, soaps, and the metallurgy of copper, gold, silver, lead, tin, and iron had attained a high degree of perfection in the Mediterranean world; especially in Egypt. Pure science—mathematics, physics, and astronomy—had been developed also to a remarkable degree.

Unfortunately, we have no information concerning the laboratories of the great physicists of the antique world. In all probability they surrounded their experiments and their means of action by a certain mystery calculated to enhance their prestige and to maintain their influence. Therefore we only know ancient science by its results. These are sometimes surprising. Without speaking of the many enigmas propounded by Egyptian civilization, we can cite Heron of Alexandria who handed down brilliant inventions; in particular his "fountain," a kind of miniature geyser, and his "aeolipile," or recoil steam engine. We know that recoil engines have been tested during recent years (cars with fuses by Fritz von Opel) which would be the ideal solution for stratospheric travel at high speed. On the other hand, we are acquainted with the works of the great mathematician Archimedes and the burning mirrors with which, we are told, he destroyed the fleet besieging Syracuse, by concentrating the light of the sun on the wooden boats.

But it is necessary to make an immense leap forward into time and reach the eighth century (Geber), or even the twelfth, before seeing the rudimentary ancestor of the modern laboratory. Al Farabi, Avicenna, and Averroes were true chemists, like the great Roger Bacon, the inventor of cannon powder. Another two centuries elapse before the appearance of the most brillant alchemists: Albert the Great, Arnaud de Villeneuve, Raymond Lulle, and many others, all passionately devoted to the pursuit of the philsophers' stone.

One of the greatest surprises brought about by the progress of science is certainly the experimental demonstration of the principle invoked by the alchemists and the justification of their endeavors. The transmutation of bodies, still qualified as chimerical by contemporary dictionaries, has been an accomplished fact for several years. Indeed the first transmutation was obtained by Rutherford in 1919, and since then—but especially during the last two or three years—a great number have been realized. True, the quantities obtained are still imponderable, and the interest of these discoveries is purely scientific. But the *principle* of the mutability of atoms is admitted today. And that is the important fact, for up to the present time the dogma of the eternal, indivisible, and unalterable atom, dominated all science and only began to be shaken when radioactivity was discovered. Though the methods used (particle bombardment and potentials of several million volts) are very different from those available to the alchemists, it is nevertheless fitting to make honorable amends and to regret that the authors of our encyclopedias and many classical books thought themselves authorized to ridicule the magnificent efforts of men whose wide-ranging minds were, after all, on the right track. Evidently they did not clothe their thoughts in the garb which today enables our efforts to be accessible to everyone. But they had their reasons for this, and did not even Taine write that science was not healthy for everyone? The wholesale manufacture of mediocrities does not multiply the Lavoisiers nor the Pasteurs, but contributes to the endorsement of a number of false ideas among the public. These ideas are sometimes harmful, as they are hastily deduced from extrapolations based on insufficient experiments and prematurely popularized for the needs of a cause often unrelated to science.

Paracelcus, a brilliant professor of medicine and chemistry in Basle (1527), seems to have been the first doctor to have a laboratory. The systematic studies that he made on medicines are still in use today: opium, mercury, sulphur, antimony and arsenic. In those days, a laboratory was infinitely picturesque. It is generally portrayed as a vaulted room, encumbered with a motley assortment of objects; open in-folios, stuffed animals, gasmeters, a mattress, and alembics with wood furnaces. The alchemist is always old; he has a noble head adorned by a long beard. He wears a magnificent coat. Painters could not help being impressed by the beautiful light and shade of such a picture. For many people the word "laboratory" still evokes Faust.

When we picture the conditions under which our predecessors were obliged to work, when we think of the infinite difficulties to be surmounted in making the smallest experiment, we are filled with admiration at the results. Today our physical efforts are reduced to a minimum; dealers in chemical products offer us any number of bodies at different degrees of purity. The scientist of the past was obliged to manufacture or produce them himself. We connect instruments in a few seconds with the help of glass tubes that we bend and weld by means of the docile gas flame. We make tight and supple joints with rubber corks and the assemblage of apparatus is simplified by rubber tubes in all diameters and all thicknesses. The scientists of old had to make their joints of various clays or cements; their tubes were of sandstone or baked clay, their supple tubes of leather. Their only combustion was charcoal, and they had no way of knowing the temperature of the reactions. We have running water on our tables; they had to draw it in a wooden pail. We have air and all gases under pressure; they had only leather bellows. And yet they could distinguish, prepare, and describe such complex bodies as corrosive sublimate, ammonia, pyroacetic acid (the ardent spirit of Riplée), mercuric sulphides, nitric acid, cannon powder and numerous coloring materials, to say nothing of the poisons. It is impossible for the layman to imagine the obstacles they overcame, nor the talent, ingenuity, skill, and infinite patience of which they gave proof.

Nicolas Lémery created the first large chemical laboratory. From 1672 this brilliant mind enjoyed signal success and great celebrity. All the chemists of his time in the whole of Europe were trained at his school. We will have occasion to return to this farther on. That same year a magnificent work, illustrated with superb engravings which set forth in detail the celebrated experiments on vacuum by Otto de Guericke, was published in Amsterdam six years after the death of its author, the Jesuit, Gaspard Schott. One of the plates, that of the famous hemispheres of Magdebourg, has been reproduced the world over. Cultured Europe became passionately interested in Science.

Let us now pass to the eighteenth century, a time when laboratories were the fashion. Voltaire, who himself studied physics and mathematics and translated Newton in the Chateau de Cirey with the Marquise du Châtelet, informs us that Philippe, Duke of Orleans, had his own laboratory. The Abbé Nollet, Professor of Physics and Natural History to the royal children of France, frequented the "Salons" and revealed the first mysteries of electricity to his aristocratic listeners in an attractive form. The engravings, and especially the frontispiece, which illustrate his *Essay on the Electricity of Bodies* (1746) are delightful, for they show the efforts of the designers to give instruments the elegance imposed by the taste of the period. As the physical laboratory was a drawing room in the style of Louis XV or of the Regency, it seemed necessary to gracefully curve the spokes of the wheels and the feet of the stands, and to artistically carve the copper spigots and all metallic pieces. The esthetics of instruments evolves and follows the fashion. The instruments of today are chromium plated, black, and sharply outlined. Those made before the war were grey and gold.

The laboratory of one of the world's greatest scientists, Lavoisier, the founder of modern chemistry, was also a drawing room, if we can judge from the magnificent portrait by David which now hangs in the Library of the Rockefeller Institute in New York. In this latter case, however, it is only right to add that a part of his work was done in quarters which had an oven and a chimney, whereas his physiological experiments were made in a large, light, clean, and tidy room as is shown by a sketch of Madame Lavoisier.

I have only spoken of chemical and physical laboratories because till then there were hardly any others that could be called such. Biology and physiology did not exist as experimental sciences. The first physiological experiments were those of Lavoisier and of Laplace. They demonstrated that respiration can be likened to a combustion and measurements were thus introduced into biology.

On the other hand, the contemplative sciences—those of pure observation and those that do not require predetermined experiments as a basic method of investigation, such as botany, geology, astronomy, etc.—do not entail the necessity of a real laboratory. It can be said therefore that the laboratory was not systematically used in the biological sciences before Pasteur and Claude Bernard. Bernard, Professor of medicine at the College de France and professor of physiology at the Faculty of Sciences, had relatively good facilities as he occupied an already well established professorship. On the contrary, Pasteur, the great revolutionary professor of chemistry, found himself faced with unbelievable difficulties from the very start, for he was an active innovator. Lack of space prevents me from dwelling on this subject as much as I should like, and René-Vallery-Radot has already done so brilliantly. I will simply cite a few sentences of one of Pasteur's first disciples, the great chemist Emile Duclaux:

When Raulin, Pasteur's chief assistant, took up his duties, the laboratory beneath the cellar had been given back to the rats, its legitimate proprietors. A very small building on the rue d'Ulm, built as a counterpart to the caretaker's lodge, had just been put at the disposal of Pasteur. It had been well-nigh impossible to construct an incubator which was indispensable for studying fermentations. Pasteur had built one in the well of the stairs, but he could only go in on his knees. Nevertheless, I have seen him spending many long hours there, for it is in this tiny incubator that all the studies on spontaneous generation were made and where the thousands of vessels employed for his celebrated experiments were daily examined. The movement which revolutionized the science of physical man, in all its aspects, started in this tiny hovel which we would hesitate to use as a rabbit hutch.

We must admit that this last sentence surpasses in pathos the most moving poetic fantasy when we consider all the consequences that followed—the creation of bacteriology, sterile surgery, the prophylaxy of contagious diseases, curative sera, preventive vaccines, the treatment of hydrophobia, pasteurization of milk, of wine, of beer, the salvage of serici-culture and many others.

It is important to fully explain the modern trend of the sciences of life before giving a brief outline of the ideal laboratory for experimental medicine—such a laboratory does not as yet exist anywhere. I dwelt at length on this subject in the first chapter and will therefore merely remind the reader briefly of the ideas I developed previously and which, moreover, can be found in substance in the writings of Claude Bernard.

Laboratories for experimental medicine, physiology, or general biology differ from others in two main respects. First, by their equipment, which must naturally be adapted to the variety of their problems, and secondly, one could even say mostly, by their spirit, which is at present in an evolutive phase.

Indeed, nature is one. When a flower grows and blossoms, when a bird flies, when a child is born, when any phenomenon occurs numerous forces enter into play: chemical reactions, mechanical and electrical forces, pressures, and tensions which are made manifest to our senses by colors, odors, sounds, heat, movements, weight, hardness, and fragility. When man, after having for centuries confused science and philosophy, wanted to systematize and catalogue his impressions so as to attempt an explanation of their causes and foresee their effects, he was obliged to group them as simply as possible into distinct classes as a result of the rapid increase in the number of observations. He therefore created arbitrary categories, which seemed logical and which in any case were necessary, such as zoology, medicine, chemistry, physics, etc. These were further divided into other groups and sub-groups: physiology, pathology, cytology, embryology, mineral and organic chemistry, and molecular and atomic physics.

From the standpoint of the global phenomena—the flower, the bird, the child—it is evident that this classification has no meaning. It is impossible to separate in a blossoming rose the chemical reactions that have resulted in the production of its fragance from those that determined the color of the petals, from those that presided over the development of the grain, over the fixation of the carbonic acid of the air, over the elaboration of the sap, or of the solid structure. It is impossible to separate these from the correlative physical phenomena: osmotic pressure of the sap; equilibrium of the membranes, phototropism, absorption and reflection of the light by the pigments, photocapillary and capillary phenomena of all kinds. It is equally impossible to separate them from botany. Each group of chemical or physical facts evidently corresponds to one or several biological problems; each isolated biological fact is the expression of a series of chemical and physical facts. It is evident that the same reasoning can be applied to every living being. That is what I meant when I wrote, "nature is one." There is only one science. It is our ignorance, the infirmity of our senses, and our need to understand which have created *the sciences.*

The individual is the unit of the biological phenomenon. The units of the physical and chemical phenomena are the molecule, the atom, and the electron. The positron, the neutron, etc. are the units of the subatomic phenomena which are the constituents of *all* matter. Phenomena on the same scale and of the same order of dimensions were naturally classified together by the human mind, and this division into "compartments" often does not correspond to any other more fundamental difference.

The preceding lines have perhaps enabled the reader to understand the necessary complexity of a laboratory of general biology when we include in this term all the sciences of life. The abundance and variety of the problems inevitably lead to a division of the work, and at the present stage we are obliged to resort to specialists who study biological chemistry on the one hand, physiology on the other, medicine separately, etc., each of these categories being themselves divided into others. But when practical problems of immediate necessity or very special problems are put aside in order to try and arrive at an understanding of important fundamental problems as a whole—such as the nervous system, immunity, the functions of endocrine glands, cancer and many others—it is absolutely necessary to organize a laboratory, a department, or even an institute of pure research *where all disciplines are represented.* This is apparently the principal difference between the laboratory of the past and the one of today; the different spirit I mentioned above. We are no longer satisfied by a purely biological answer when we know that underlying mechanisms of a physicochemical nature exist at the base of a phenomenon. The division into compartments has played its part. We want to free ourselves from the arbitrary boundaries that we at first imposed upon ourselves, and we now aspire to a deeper knowledge of elementary facts that will enable us to grasp the unity and harmony of nature.

The "splendid isolation" of medicine and of the other sciences is a thing of the past. The partitions are crumbling rapidly and no one can boast of being independent. It is absolutely essential to call upon the other sciences. Chemists, who long ago borrowed the instruments and methods of physicists, are beginning to consider—often reluctantly it is true—the necessity of learning a little more physics and physicochemistry. The physicist who deals with the structure of matter is obliged to know some chemistry. The doctor himself, if he wants to do research work to understand and follow modern experiments, if he

wants to get to the bottom of things, know how our organs work and the true nature of a functional disturbance, will in the near future have to know some mathematics, physics, and chemistry. He will also have to equip his laboratories with a number of instruments which would have appeared out of place only thirty years ago. The first sign of the collapse of the partitions was the birth of mongrel sciences which are astride of two or three disciplines and which are not viable when taken separately. They are "connecting sciences" of the scientific front, those which establish the contact across "no-man's-land" and which do the work of the pioneer; of the scout. Physicochemistry, biochemistry, and biophysics, for example, are slowly growing in importance.

Representatives of the so-called exact sciences are sometimes tempted not to consider medicine as a science, simply because it has not yet attained the stage of measurements. This is unfair, for it is the most complicated science of all, not only because all the sciences enter into play in a living organism, but because the harmonious evolution of the living being in time, *his duration*, involves problems of correlation and subordination that the exact sciences are far from having solved. It can certainly be stated that medicine as an experimental science is still in its infancy; that it is still in the phase of making an inventory of its subjects. This is due in part to the slow progress of the elementary sciences of which it is tributary. The physiologist and then the immunologist can start from solid foundations only when chemistry can tell the biologist the exact structure of a protein—and in a few years medicine will then advance rapidly. If scientific medicine is still embryonic, it is not the fault of the doctors who have to face practical problems of immediate urgency but of the chemists and physicists who for a long time refused to face the obstacle, knowing full well that it was a difficult one to overcome.

That is why it must be stated, and constantly restated, that the progress of medicine depends on a close collaboration between pure experimental research, physiology, immunology, and serology—in a word, all the

sciences dealing with the functions and the reactions of living organisms—
and the others, chemistry and physics. The doctor, the physiologist
are forever setting problems that they are incapable of solving because
of their culture and specialization. The number of chemists and physicists who are interested in them is small. It must increase. But if the
collaboration is to be efficacious, it must exist in fact and not only in
principle. As these problems are the most difficult of all and, as the path
has been barely traced, it is necessary to call upon the "elite" and to
give them the possibility of working under the best possible conditions.
That is the price of success.

We have apparently diverged from the laboratory. But what I have
said was indispensable to enable the reader to understand the following
delineation of what a laboratory of experimental medicine should be
today. The most perfect modern laboratory seems to me to be the one just
built in Upsala, Sweden. It is devoted solely to physicochemistry. Fundamental problems of life and medicine could be studied in such a laboratory with only a few changes in some details; nothing similar exists
today. The best, to my knowledge, is still the Rockefeller Institute in
New York, but some of the buildings are already old and nothing is more
quickly outmoded than a laboratory. Dr Flexner has been the director
since its foundation in 1905, and at that time he already had the immense
merit of understanding the modern necessities of experimental medicine.
He was the first to apply the principles established by Bernard of bringing
together doctors, physiologists, and chemists and of giving them facilities for work that were unique in the world. He surrounded himself
with men who were young and gifted and left them absolutely free to
work on problems of pure science, without looking for any immediate
practical application. Our great compatriot Carrel, who was thirty-two
years old, was one of them. The harvest was magnificent, and the Rockefeller Institute truly played the role of pioneer in that line. Science can
be grateful to Dr Flexner who, before anyone else, dared to put into
practice on a large scale the ideas of Claude Bernard by adapting them
to his times.

The plan, the main lines of which I will briefly sketch, may at first seem a little strange to certain readers, for we unconsciously become slaves of our working habits and thoughts. I hope, however, that this impression will disappear if they make the necessary effort to liberate themselves from preconceived ideas.

The modern institute or research laboratory must resemble a factory more than a monument. At the end of twenty years a factory is outdated; so is a laboratory. It is no longer equal to its task, no matter what efforts are made to modernize it, and the cost of doing this is considerable at the end of this lapse of time. The conclusion is therefore that instead of erecting expensive and palatial buildings, that are costly to demolish, a scientific institute must be constructed solidly but not extravagantly, to last for a period of twenty years. It is naturally preferable to build in the country where it is sheltered from vibrations and electric perturbations. No grand staircase, no superfluous decorations, but the air pressure throughout the building should be maintained slightly above the pressure of the atmosphere, by means of big blast engines, so as to distribute filtered and humidified air heated at 20º C. [68º F.]—"conditioned" following the new term—through the hallways. Dust will thus be suppressed, as windows will not have to be opened and the air will always pass from the inside to the outside. If the total volume of air in each room is renewed two or three times an hour, the ventilation will be perfect and working conditions excellent, even in the cellars (where the most delicate instruments should be placed) and in the dark rooms, without windows, which should be numerous. Indeed, whenever it is necessary to use light to study a phenomenon, it is preferable to be in a dark room and to employ only artificial light which has the immense advantage of remaining constant and can be regulated at will. Modern photographers have understood this well, and the old painter's studio has long since disappeared.

All the rooms must be maintained at the same temperature day and night, with the exception of those consecrated to special purposes. This constant temperature is fundamental, for the slightest fluctuation destroys the adjustments of sensitive instruments and of the thermostats. There are many institutes where the heat is cut off everyday at six o'clock and from Saturday until Monday. In the winter it is impossible to work in them during the evenings or on Sundays. On Monday mornings, when it is cold, all the instruments are out of order and valuable time is lost.

All the pipes for hot water, compressed air, gas, and electricity, should be accessible in the hallways and arranged in such a way that any repair or change of distribution can be effected quickly and economically. Pipes built into walls have a certain advantage for private residences, but have been the cause of grave difficulties in laboratories. So as to simplify the construction and decrease the cost, workrooms should be identical in principle, except for a special purpose. Everything must be foreseen so that when required a laboratory can be transformed without great expense and used for another type of research.

This, naturally, entails the standardization of mobile elements; tables, chairs, lamps, and brackets, so that articles manufactured in series can be utilized and be interchangeable. All needs for any problem must be thought out ahead of time as far as possible so that work can be accomplished under the best conditions of comfort, precision, and security. There are still a certain number of distinguished scientists who have been accustomed to making their experiments with bits of wood, wire, miscellaneous pieces and makeshift means and who therefore cannot conceive doing without. I may be wrong, but I believe this is a false and archaic concept. The time passed in mounting instruments that exist on the market, under conditions that make their functioning a feat of ingenuity, seems to me a waste of time, and I think that lack of funds is often at the bottom of it. Would those who thus "tinker" with remarkable talent be as numerous if they were offered the ten, twenty, or thirty thousand francs that a good instrument costs every time they needed one? Waste of time is rarely felt, but when a distinguished mind is in question it is more serious than a waste of money.

Chemical laboratories should naturally have a special flooring and be supplied with a powerful exhaust fan for noxious gases. The operation rooms in the physiological laboratories, should have special lighting without projected shadows. There should be cold rooms, hot rooms at 37° C—photography, glass-blowing, and machine and carpentry shops. It must be possible to construct a large number of instruments rapidly on the spot. The store room should be well stocked with apparatus and chemical products so as to avoid loss of time—and the cages for experimental animals should be on the roof to ensure both the health of the animals and the absence of smells. A small meeting room and a library are also necessary.

This picture evidently diverges slightly from the usual concept of a biological or medical laboratory. But up till now the biologist has willingly abandoned his problem the moment it became chemical or physicochemical, remarking that "this is no longer in my line." Neither was it, as yet, in the line of the chemist or the physicist, who had no reason to be interested. Thus, an immense number of important questions remained only partly solved. Considerable time has been lost on account of this attitude. In the last thirty years, however, a certain number of physiologists have had the courage to go farther and have acquired the necessary knowledge to tackle the problem to the end. The results were brilliant, and the young generation, encouraged by the example of their elders, seems determined to make the considerable effort needed for the supplementary study of mathematics and chemistry. They themselves do not generally hope to be capable of solving all the chemical, physical, and mathematical problems, but they have understood that they must at least be able to direct intelligently the efforts of one or two specialized collaborators. Among other examples we have the laboratory of Professor Lapicque, who occupies the chair of Claude Bernard at the Sorbonne. His magnificent work on the muscles, nerves, and mechanism of the nervous influx, carried out in collaboration with Madame Lapicque cannot be understood without a fairly extensive knowledge of physics. This can be ascertained by reading his books or the brilliant thesis of one of his young pupils, A. M. Monnier. We must admit that these examples are less frequent in France than in other countries. An English physicist, A. V. Hill, recently drew the attention of scientists all over the world by his analysis of the mechanism of muscular contraction and fatigue.

The most important information regarding the blood, from a medical standpoint, was given by the chemists, Van Slyke, Henderson, and their pupils. The collaboration of a doctor, Avery, and a chemist, Heidelberger, resulted in one of the most notable contributions to immunology and to a knowledge of the pneumococcus, the bacterium which causes pneumonia. Finally, the Nobel Prize has just been awarded to Landsteiner, one of the most brilliant figures of modern science whose essentially chemical works on immunity are a landmark in the history of science. Examples actually abound, and I regret that I am unable to cite more of them.

The laboratory of pure medical research must be therefore a comprehensive institute where all disciplines collaborate—a kind of autonomous cell where all the efforts tend towards the same goal and where the crossfire of all methods of investigation can be directed on a single problem. Immediate methods for curing diseases will not always be sought in such an institute. The fundamental aim should be to discover differences which exist between health and sickness, between life and death. When this goal has been reached, the rest will come more easily, but we are far from having attained it. Momentarily and for many years to come, the pure clinician, in collaboration with the serologist, must continue his struggle against disease along the road already traced. The doctor is the present—the laboratory is the future.

I realize that for the great majority, certain sentences lack the power to evoke an image. When one speaks of scientific research, with the appropriate tone of conviction, the lips articulate sounds, but these sounds are not, in general, accompanied by any thought either in the mind of the speaker or in the mind of the listener. The sequence of instantaneous pictures, which almost always follows the statement of a fact, of a quality, or of an action, is missing. The layman does not "see" the work of the laboratory. And as everybody has his or her own special idea, sometimes picturesque but often false, and as a form of shyness prevents any questions from being asked, the wall that separates the scientist and the layman subsists. Pure research has always suffered from the misunderstanding caused by this wall; this ignorance. If the cultivated public had the impression of knowing what takes place in a pure research institute, it would perhaps be interested in the process of research; in the evolution of the creative thought of the scientist. If this interest existed, the contact between them would be established and those who have the means would perhaps be less reluctant to open their purses if they realized more clearly what could be accomplished with their money.

In my chapter on "Tissue Culture in Vitro," I described at length this remarkable method due to Alexis Carrel, and I outlined the consequences and possible applications. But the earlier stage remains mysterious. I showed the flower and the fruit; from the psychological point of view, it is the history of evolution, commencing from the seed, which is important.

"You speak of problems," said a friend, "but how and why do you choose them? And when your choice has been made, what happens? Are there any rules to the game? What are they? What psychological method do you use? What determines your line of approach and the techniques you employ? How do you interpret the experimental results? How do you discern the path to follow?"

I do not know if the answers I could make to these questions would be of any general interest. I am tempted to believe the contrary, for every scientist uses a personal method in conformity with his culture, his education, his habits of thought, and his character. It is certainly the last thing about which he will speak. Most of the time he acts instinctively without bothering to disengage the part of responsibility that belongs to the master who has formed him, to his environment, or to his own genius. Before analyzing the mechanisms of research I must therefore warn the reader against any generalizations and leave the door open to other possibilities.

It is evident that the choice of a problem depends on many factors. It is never completely free but more or less dominated by a man's profession. A chemist will attack a chemical problem; a biologist, a biological problem. A young man will be influenced by his professor. These contingencies lose some of their value as one advances in age and the brain, like a magnetic needle, turns irresistibly to the problems which attract it, irrespective of the narrow boundaries in which it had been imprisoned by the necessary division of the sciences into compartments. Those who are capable of freeing themselves from these scholastic disciplines are rare, but they are the ones who open new paths. The most illustrious example in France is Pasteur, chemist and physicist, whose genius led him to create bacteriology outright. In America, Jacques Loeb, a doctor, sheds a flood of light on the chemistry of colloids. In England, a physicist, Hill, becomes one of the most celebrated physiologists. In Germany, Helmholtz, a universal spirit, leaves a brilliant trace in every realm.

As a general rule, the amplitude of the problem is a gauge of the value of the man who dares to attack it. Small, limited problems, details which can probably never lead to unexplored regions, attract all the modest workers who doubt themselves—often wrongly—and who are appalled by the idea of undertaking a long and exacting work. I said "often wrongly" for, without their knowing it, these workers might well be capable of accomplishing a great task. They lack neither science nor skill, but confidence, courage, inspiration, and sometimes imagination. They suffer from an inferiority complex, following the Freudian expression. My respect for truth forces me to admit that one also meets the diametrically opposite type whose vanity and presumption rests on an incurable mediocrity or an unfathomable stupidity. Thank God, this species is more rare.

It is evident that the need to possess various kinds of knowledge increases with the generality of the problem, for the greater number of phenomena it covers the more numerous will be the paths of approach. For example, suppose one wants to study a very vast subject—immunity in infectious diseases. A doctor will naturally choose the path traced by Pasteur and his pupils:He will study experimentally the immunity from different diseases in man and in animals. It is the immediate practical problem. He will employ microbes or toxins as an antigen (substance that determines in the organism the reactions manifested by immunity). If, by any chance, he has sufficient knowledge of chemistry, he will take a chemist to work with him and they will follow the path in which Landsteiner and his pupils distinguished themselves. They were not satisfied to experiment on immunity with microbes and toxins which are complex and little known bodies, but took as a goal the study of the very mechanism of immunity in general and injected well-defined chemical products into experimental animals, thus simplifying and defining the problem. If, on the other hand, our doctor has any knowledge of physics, he will try, either alone or in collaboration with a physicist, to put into practice the physical and physicochemical modifications produced in the blood by immunization and to draw conclusions from the alterations brought about in the molecules in solution in blood serum. In the last two cases he will be acting more scientifically by attempting to replace a large problem of an immensely complex science with a series of simpler problems belonging to more universal and better known sciences. In other words, he will analyze his difficulties.

But it often happens that as a result of intelligent observations suggested by his daily, commonplace work, a scientist is put on the road leading to a discovery, or a series of important discoveries, without having given himself a problem, or without having foreseen the scope of the developments of his researches. There are many examples of a mediocre, matter-of-fact start ending in a fundamental work: Lavoisier seems to have become interested in the problem of combustion because he was asked to study the question of lighting by candles. This led him to elucidate the mechanisms of the respiration of animals, which he was the first to assimilate with combustion and so destroy forever the universally admitted but false phlogistic hypothesis. Pasteur was led to microorganisms by experiments that were in no way biological. His studies on

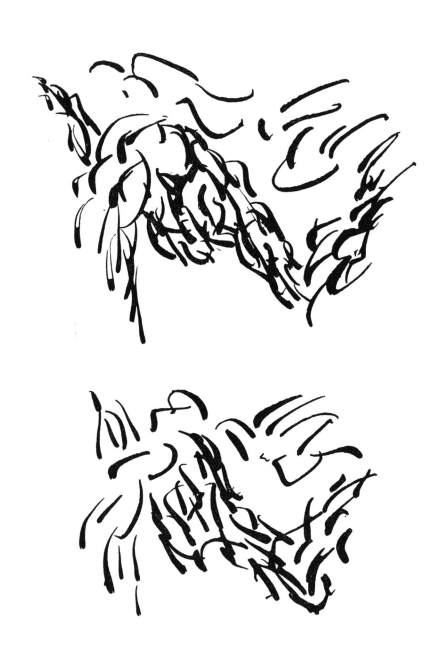

sodium tartrate and paratartrate enabled him to discover crystalline asymmetry which awakened his interest in moulds and, by a remarkably rigorous sequence of ideas, gradually led him to the study of fermentations and then on to the discovery of microbes.

In former days, when the sciences were in an embryonic state, great discoveries were made by men who were simply gifted, intelligent, and favored by chance circumstances that enabled their brains to find the right channel. Denis Papin, a medical doctor who grasped the power of steam, invented the first engine and the first centrifuge pump in 1688. Joseph Henry, an actor and dramatic author, was traveling with his small company and enjoying great success when he fell ill. A friend gave him a book of vulgarization to amuse him during his convalescence. Rather vague answers were given in it to questions such as: why does the flame of a candle always point upwards? Why does a magnet attract iron? Henry became passionately interested in these problems, and when he was cured he disbanded his troupe, gave up the theatre and devoted himself to the study of electric and magnetic manifestations. He discovered the phenomenon known as self-induction (the unit of self-induction is now called a *henry*); became a Professor of Physics at Princeton and ended his days as director of the famous Smithsonian Institution in Washington. Finally, Sadi Carnot, an engineer but not a pure scientist, while studying steam engines from the point of view of their economic yield, published his small but great book, *Reflexions sur la Puissance Motrice du feu* in which he first laid the foundations of one of the most fundamental principles of our human science. This principle was named after him and is also known as the second principle of thermodynamics.

The preceding lines clearly show that a scientific problem is often the consequence of the unforeseen encounter of a prepared mind with a fact of observation and that its choice depends on such a large number of factors that no rules whatsoever can be applied to it.

Let us therefore admit that the attention or the curiosity of a worker has been awakened by an accidental or an instigated observation. First

101

of all, he assures himself that the experimental fact which has given birth to this observation is real and can be repeated. If this is so, and if the fact is new, the experimental stage then begins. The methods employed naturally depend on the aptitude of the researcher, his acquired knowledge, and on the technical means at his disposal. Let us suppose his experiments are made in such a way that he succeeds in *measuring;* in expressing ratios quantitatively. His first aim will be to decrease the number of variables and to reveal those which have a direct influence on the phenomenon. To accomplish this he maintains certain factors constant and, if possible, manages to vary only one at a time. Finally, he is faced with a certain number of figures which, in general, express the evolution of a phenomenon as a function of some kind of parameter—time, temperature, etc. Now he must interpret. What do these systematic and hitherto unknown variations signify?

Whenever possible, he endeavors to express them by a mathematical formula which expresses *the law of the phenomenon.* The problem is thus well defined, for mathematics applied to the sciences is only a precise language, a kind of mental stenography as the philosopher Mach expressed it, which, by means of a few conventional symbols, enables us to economize thought and time.

At this point hypothesis, the most powerful instrument of scientific research, comes into play. I will describe it briefly, since I cannot dwell on it as long as I should like. When a phenomenon has been thoroughly studied and isolated from a whole, when its variations can be predicted, it is important to explain its mechanism by means of already known elements in order to establish its connection between the anterior facts and to assure the progression of the science on solid foundations without a break in continuity. *The scientific hypothesis therefore consists of the picture one draws of the causes and consequences of a series of observed acts.* In other words, it is a momentary explanation, based entirely on common sense, logic, and past experiments, of the reason why the fact is produced. It is an explanation which locates the new phenomenon in a series of events, only a certain number of which are known and which establishes a correlation between them which allows one to infer the existence of unknown, intermediary phenomena. We thus see the double role of the hypothesis. This fragile structure, born of our brain, forces us to *imagine original experiments* or new instruments with the purpose of revealing the existence of a hitherto unknown fact to consolidate it, or else to invalidate it definitively—in which case we abandon it. For we must never forget that a hypothesis must only be a tool, to be kept as long as it is useful, but replaced by another, without hesitation, as soon as it is found to be in disaccord with the facts. A hypothesis must be a ladder, not a cage.

Imagination should therefore play an important role, and scientific work is thus related to creative, artistic work. It is also related, through its esthetic sense, to the search after that special beauty, the harmony of the world, as Henri Poincaré wrote in *Science et Methode,* a book that is remarkable for its clarity of thought. There is, however, a fundamental difference between the artist and scientist. The artist enjoys complete liberty and can always follow his fantasy, for he is not obliged to rediscover the road of truth, the hidden path of the sequence of facts in an unknown jungle. Personality dominates everything in the arts and in literature, while science must remain impersonal. "Art is I—Science is We." The personality, the originality of the scientist can manifest itself only in the methods, the means brought into play to obtain the results, and not in the results themselves.

Scientific thought, like the nature it proposes to analyze in human symbols, is one, and it endeavors to discover the hidden process—the *latens processus* of Francis Bacon. This process unites and cements the different degrees of evolution perceived by our mosaic and periodic perception of the hidden order—the *latens schematismus* of the same philosopher—which is at the bottom of our sense perceptions. The real order, outside our sphere, the subjects which pass behind us and whose shadow alone is seen at the far end of the cave, to speak like Plato, escapes our direct observation. This is not important if we know how to project the results of our mental efforts outside ourselves, and if this projection is merged with the sensorial reactions determined in us by real objects.

I will give only one example of the role of a hypothesis, for it is a subject familiar to all. But I will choose one of the most brilliant, one of the most fruitful, which has emerged from a human brain. Experiments were being made in Pasteur's laboratory in 1880 on chicken cholera, a terrible disease which kills 90 % of the birds in a flock. The cultures of the microbes, seeded without interruption every twenty-four hours, kept their virulence. Great was the surprise, when a forgotten culture, which was a few weeks old, was used and the inoculated chickens became ill but did not die. *The virulence was attenuated.* Pasteur instantaneously grasped the significance between this occurrence and the fact that in many illnesses the person who has contracted the infection and recovered from it, acquires a resistance; a natural immunity. He thus noted for the first time that the virulence of microbes can attenuate itself, and by a magnificent flight of fancy he immediately seized the importance of the parallel and emitted the hypothesis that in future it would be possible to vaccinate against infectious diseases. I will not dwell on the feverish activity which seized the whole staff when he developed his idea. It was the dawn of new medicine rising on the horizon. From that moment all experiments were directed in the same lines and ended in the well-known triumphant confirmation.

Things, unfortunately, do not always end as happily. But the coordinated experimental phase which follows the hypothesis is nevertheless the most thrilling of all. Words seem incapable—I only blame my incompetence as a writer—of evoking the unforgettable hours passed in the laboratory, face to face with the instruments often conceived by oneself for a special purpose, while following the progress of an experiment with a beating heart.

In the silence, accentuated rather than lessened by the soft hum of the revolving machines, the muffled throbbing of a transformer, or the slight beats of the recording instrument which divides the minutes into equal parts, the little pieces of brilliant metal, despairingly indifferent, bring us with impartial impassibility the answer we are awaiting. Then we are really conscious of having achieved a victory; a victory of the mind over mysterious, wily matter finally forced to surrender one of its secrets.

Undoubtedly every scientist has known similar minutes; the setting alone changes. One scientist will evoke a specimen examined under the microscope; another, a chemical reaction in a fragile vessel; a third, a simple sheet of paper covered by symbols; and yet another, the dark room where the photographic plate progressively reveals the longed-for picture. But all have been intoxicated by the same emotion, otherwise they would not be true researchers. An element of emotional sentiment is necessary in every creative career. With the scientist it is not exteriorized. It nevertheless exists, for the scientist must possess enthusiasm. Descartes said that to be deprived of enthusiasm was a sign of mediocrity. Pasteur extolling the word itself, bequeathed to us by the Greeks—Entheos, an eternal god—wrote that enthusiasm represents in the search for material truth what faith represents in the search for spiritual truth. Without enthusiasm or belief, the quest for truth will remain unrewarded.

We have followed the scientist from the moment when, after having chosen a problem—designated by chance or by reasoning—he has begun by eliminating experimentally the secondary factors, has then studied the conditions essential for a certain phenomenon to appear and has finally been able to link it qualitatively and quantitatively to those which precede it. The hypothesis has led him to foresee certain facts: he has initiated the experiments necessary to verify these facts. He has or has not verified them. It sometimes happens, as we stated above, that in the course of such an experiment a new, unforeseen fact is observed which is extraneous to the experimental goal pursued. Discoveries are often thus grafted on to one another and finally arrive at results that were not in the least anticipated. The thread which links the discoveries together can therefore be very tenuous, but it nevertheless exists, and every time we create or perfect a technique of observation or of measurement, in order to study a problem, we are certain to discover a number of unknown facts which can be the costarting point of new investigations.

One of the most important phases of research consists of setting up the techniques. A technique consists of the combination of the material means used to obtain a certain experimental result. We can say, without exaggeration, that all the achievements realized in the scientific realm have been obtained thanks to the continual improvement of experimental techniques.

Claude Bernard, in his outstanding book, *The Introduction to Experimental Medicine*, which should be the catechism of every scientist, writes: "I am convinced that in the evolving experimental sciences, and particularly in those which are as complex as biology, the discovery of a new instrument of observation or of experimentation renders much greater services than many systematic or philosophic dissertations." Lavoisier created modern chemistry with scales. Pasteur's whole work rests on the use of the microscope. Radioactivity depends entirely on the electrometer. Our progress in the knowledge of the structure of matter is due to the spectographs and the modern instruments that utilize the properties of X-rays. Our latest acquisition in the knowledge of the intimate structure of atoms which have led to the transmutation of bodies, is based on the use of radium, of X-rays, on the technique of vacuum tubes, and on a prodigious instrument invented by C. T. R. Wilson— the expansion chamber. These are only a few examples among thousands.

Nowadays a technique or a new instrument should be considered as antennae which enable us to extend the field of action of our senses beyond their natural limits. It is thanks to them that we have attained the infinitely small and the infinitely large. We know how to measure the dimensions of a molecule within a thousand millionth of a millimeter, and we know the chemical composition of stars, whose light, traveling at three hundred thousand kilometers a second, takes five hundred years to reach us. True, we do not yet know how to cure a common cold, but this only proves that, contrary to what one might think, this last problem is even more complicated than the first. Indeed, its solution

depends on the progress of a very special and little-known chemistry: that of the fundamental substances of living matter—proteins.

The laboratory must therefore also be a shop where essential tools for the realization of an experiment can be built. This explains the considerable length of time needed to advance one step on "the rocky path which leads to truth" and which is often out of proportion to the results obtained. The equipment, the tools of a laboratory, naturally depend on the work done there. But, as I said above, the division of the sciences into different compartments decreases every day. This accounts for the steadily increasing cost of laboratories—instruments costing thousands of francs are numerous. And it is not these which cost the most. An instrument does not work alone no matter how ingenious and how beautiful it is. Even when dealing with a completely automatic instrument, which is rare, the prime necessity in research is the man, not only the scientist who conceives the experiments and interprets the results, but the assistant who, without the same culture or imagination, can yet execute the plan established by his chief.

The experimental verification of a hypothesis entails important expenditures of time and money; so important that they almost excuse the question, dreaded by scientists, that an educated man should always hesitate to ask—"Of what use will it be?"

"Of what use is a new-born child?" was already Faraday's answer. Indeed, pure research in itself constitutes not only the fundamental basis of practical science and industrial progress but also the best method for cultivating the mind; the only one capable of maintaining philosophical thought in contact with the facts it cannot ignore, no matter what its orientation.

The following example is striking. Professor George Ellery Hale, the founder and director of the Mt. Wilson Observatory, was one of the most remarkable and distinguished men I have ever met. He chose a beautiful site at the foot of the mountains where he erected laboratories consecrated to astrophysics—the physics of stars, a science which, for a very good reason, is not widespread. In Pasadena, not far from Hollywood, the laboratories consist of a group of light-colored buildings with large bay windows, flat roofs, only one floor, covered by vines, and framed by the brilliant velvet of well-cared-for lawns, separated from each other by flower-bordered paths. Flowers everywhere, the California sky, and in the background to the east the gray chain of the Rocky Mountains. Light, color, perfumes, and peace : the ideal.

When passing through New York, about fifteen years ago, Dr. Hale came to see my chief, Dr. Carrel, at the Rockefeller Institute. We talked together at length and he spoke of a disconcerting problem that I cannot explain without first bringing up some elementary notions of physics. We know that after passing through a prism, white light spreads out into a multicolored fan; violet, indigo, blue, green, yellow, orange, and red—the colors of the spectrum. The color white is the result of the combination of these elementary radiations. Just as every note of the scale corresponds to a well defined number of vibrations per second at a determined wavelength, so each color is due to a vibration of known wavelength.

It is evident that our senses are too limited to perceive the difference between wavelengths that are very close. This applies to the ear as well as to the eye. For instance, the note A corresponds to 435 vibrations per second in France, but to 440 in Germany. This is a matter of convention. The color of a spectrum is the result of the juxtaposition of a great number of pure monochromatic radiations that can only be designated by their wavelength. But the light emitted by the vapors of a metal or of a pure gas, at a high temperature, or subjected to an electric discharge after passing through a prism, gives a characteristic spectrum which is no longer continuous like that of white light but is, on the contrary, made up of brilliant rays standing out against a black background. These yellow, green, blue, or red rays are increasingly fine in proportion as they are increasingly monochromatic, and because they are due to the vibrations of the elements of the atom their place in the spectrum— namely their wavelength—is rigorously invariable. That is how the presence of gases and terrestrial metals in the spectrum of the stars has been established with certainty.

Now it had been observed at Mt. Wilson that certain rays, unquestionably due to a known element, did not occupy their usual place in the spectrum emitted by certain stars. There was a shift towards the violet. In other words, their wavelength was modified. This was a phenomenon that overruled all accepted ideas, for, as we have already stated, the characteristic wavelength of radiations is such an invariable constant, that it was even proposed as the basis for the international meter. The only known difference between the two spectra was that one of them was produced by vapors proceeding from a star and the other, as far as could be ascertained, was produced by the same vapors proceeding from an earthly source. Two hypotheses were possible. Either it was a question of a very similar metal, unknown on earth, or the very high temperature of the star, around 20,000° C., modified the aspect of the spectrum. Hale and his collaborator Anderson favored the latter hypothesis.

But the only way to transform a hypothesis into a truth is to experiment. How could this be realized? The highest temperature obtained under the best conditions was 5,800° C. (diamonds boil at around 4,200° C.) and it was necessary to reach 20,000° C., treble the heat of the sun. Most people would have been satisfied to rest on the theory, but not Hale and Anderson.

They conceived one of the most beautiful experiments in the history of science and found the means to realize it. Dr. Hale erected a powerful electric generator in one of the small, cheerful cottages of Pasadena and built huge condensers to accumulate enormous charges of electricity. In his own magnificent laboratory (another beflowered cottage) he built a metal spectrograph in which the incessant play of molecular pumps maintained an almost absolute vacuum. A thin metal thread, a few centimeters long, with a diameter equal to one or two tenths of a millimeter, was then stretched, likewise in a vacuum, between two electrodes. When everything was ready and the condenser had been charged, a switch, operated from a distance, produced a short circuit in the plates of the condensers through the tiny thread which during about one hundred thousandth of a second, was subjected to a current of several hundred horse power. A violent explosion naturally occurred; the thread was instantly vaporized and the only thing that remained to be done was to develop the plate. The spectrum obtained was almost identical to that of the star; the rays had been displaced in the same way and in the same direction. The theory and the hypothesis had been confirmed. The temperature attained—which was calculated as it could not be measured—was about 20,000° C.

The experiment cost more than a hundred thousand dollars, or approximately a million and a half francs. It resulted in no material improvement, either in transportation, bathrooms, radio, or television. It only brought another proof that human intelligence is capable of liberating itself from the limits imposed by its condition—of crossing the interstellar space that light takes hundreds of years to cover—and of annexing the stars to its domain.

We are now in 1935. The laboratory has conquered its place in the sun. But it must not be concluded from this fact and from the undeniable interest shown by a great part of the public, that scientific research has nothing more to wish for. Far from it. It is still very difficult to recruit workers who want to consecrate themselves to pure research, and who are qualified to do this. Credits have certainly increased since 1860 and a minister of education would no longer give the answer received by Pasteur: "There is no provision in the budget to enable me to give you fifty centimes for your experimental expenses." But though the funds exist nowadays, they are always inadequate; especially when pure science is concerned.

Public interest in scientific things, which is largely due to curiosity or to a fad, has always existed—it is not a characteristic of our time. It was difficult, around 1675, to proceed along the rue Galande. Not only did a noisy crowd of students dash down the narrow street, but it was also congested by coaches, adorned with heraldic bearings, bringing lords and princes, and by sedan chairs carrying great ladies. The attraction was a backyard lighted by the gleam of the furnaces where Nicolas

Lémery, a young man but a great chemist, was lecturing. He taught in Paris for twenty-five years and attained great popularity. It reached such a point that after having filled his house with pupils, he had to occupy almost all of the rue Galande in order to house those who kept presenting themselves and was obliged to run a sort of *table d'hôte* in his own house to provide food for those who solicited the honor of being admitted to listen to him.

In 1675, he published his *Cours de Chimie*. This work acquired such an extraordinary success and immense popularity that, despite many pirated copies, a new edition had to be published almost every year. It was circulated in every civilized country and translated into Latin, English, German, Italian, Spanish, and perhaps into other languages as well. The author was called the Great Lémery.

If publishers are to be believed, chemical treatises are far from enjoying a similar success in our so-called enlightened epoch when the population has more than doubled and everyone knows how to read. This is equally true of all scientific works.

Science no more than art, enriches a man. Judging from the salaries allotted to scientists throughout the world, this seems to be one of the rare points on which all people agree. In certain countries, however, they are more affluent than in France. This may be due to the fact that people believe that the man who consecrates himself to science deeply loves his profession and his work therefore amuses him. It might almost be considered as a kind of revenge on the part of those whose work bores them, but I do not think so. It is more the result of a habit, perpetuated by the disinterestedness of scientific workers; their absence of unity, and especially by the fact that the public does not realize the prime necessity of pure science and the enormous expense it invariably entails.

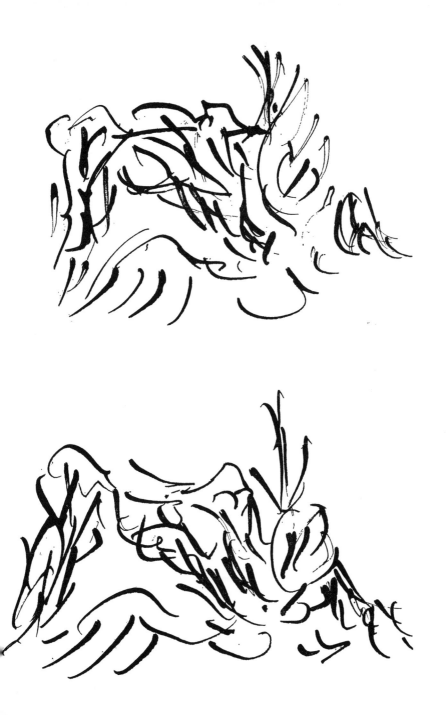

THE ILLUSIONS OF SCIENCE 1936

We often take it for granted that when a word has been defined everyone gives it the same meaning. This assumption is false. A certain number of words, especially monosyllables such as life, soul, God, law, king, and gold, evoke not only very different ideas but very different emotions in different individuals. They are too fertile. They symbolize a combination of objective and subjective concepts which are so complex that we cannot hope to meet many men who will react identically to all the psychological and logical impressions raised by these words when the subject or idea they represent is thoroughly studied.

They do not usually lead to errors, which is fortunate. When they are used in a drawing room we know that everyone will understand their meaning and we have the impression that there is perfect agreement as long as they are only accessories in a sentence. But if one of them is dissected more closely, it immediately becomes apparent that certain people give it a special significance. If a discussion is started, dissensions spring up where a perfect accord seemed to exist at first. The more these terms are analyzed the deeper are the divergences, and we soon discover that instead of two or three groups discussing amicably together we are faced with individuals who suddenly seem less congenial.

These fundamental words have tremendous symbolic power. The meaning given to them by a man is not only a personal definition which he believes objective, but unbeknownst to himself it is also an exact portrayal of his character, namely an outline of his psychological evolution or a summary of his family traditions. His ancestral heritage or his sentimental revolts are thus exteriorized. The word itself is only a pretext, so that if two human beings give it the same interpretation, it signifies a relation of ideas, sentiments, and character much deeper than is implied by the usual accord on the meaning of an ordinary term.

To a certain degree, the word "science" belongs in this category. Being purely objective, it does not raise violent divergences. Nevertheless, the term is not clear for everyone and possesses a certain prestige which, unfortunately, rests on an erroneous or incomplete idea of its significance. Scientists, fortunately, have something better to do than to enlighten the public on this subject, and it is easier for them to accept the relative consideration accorded to their profession, though in France this does not compensate for the financial inconvenience of modest circumstances. It may therefore be useful if not to define science at least to describe its aims, its intellectual approach, the weak points of its methods, and discuss the value of the answers it can give. We may then be able to determine the origin of certain illusions and discover the source of certain misunderstandings.

The aim of science is to understand and explain the evolution of natural phenomena by studying the relations which exist between them. The external world is revealed to us by our senses, intermediaries that are as necessary for our knowledge as is the receiving set for diffusing music. What remains of the universe if we suppress man? No human being can have the slightest idea of it. Things only borrow their reality and their aspect when an instrument, the eye, is interposed in the path of radiations and transforms them into chemical or physicochemical energy. The nerves transport a part of this energy to the brain which "sees" the objects, their shadows, their colors. We therefore know that these colors are only the physiological translation of a periodic physical phenomenon of high frequency characterized by a given "wavelength" for each color. The color yellow simply expresses the reaction of certain of our cells when a radiation with a wavelength of 0.570 to 0.590 thousandth of a millimeter strikes them; namely, when they are excited by the same phenomenon repeated 520 trillion times per second. Yellow light in itself has no color. The notion is entirely subjective. The same observation holds true for all our senses. Lack of space prevents our giving other examples, but these facts have been frequently studied and explained by numerous authors. It is impossible to discuss the nature of events which will always escape us and which moreover do not interest us except from a speculative point of view. The term "knowledge" has no significance when it is applied to things that cannot be conceived. Our perceptions are the very foundation of our universe; the universe we discuss. The fact that in reality it is obscure and silent is of no importance if our mere presence transforms it into the marvel that we admire. It matters little that the rainbow exists only in the back of our eyes if we thereby gain the possibility of taking it with us everywhere after the rain, as soon as a sunbeam pierces the clouds.

Philosophers of all times have drawn this distinction between the two concepts of the universe. Plato, in his famous parable of the cave, has given the idea its most celebrated form, and yet the basis for his reasoning was not provided by the science of his day. Only pure genius enabled him to attain it by a prodigious short cut.

Thus, only one of the two faces of the world is known to us. Can we even speak of the existence of the second? We are the unconscious and purely mechanical translators, and at the same time the readers and commentators, of a work the essence of which escapes us. We can never hope to pass the boundaries of the realm limited by our senses if we only utilize the documents they give us.

The brief summary we gave of the proposed aims of science is therefore transformed into the following: "Science aims to describe *the succession of sensorial events determined in us by phenomena of the exter-*

117

nal world. It tries to summarize in a brief formula the relations existing between certain groups of facts." Every time it succeeds in doing this, it enables us to foresee the future to a certain extent. We then say that it has established a scientific law. It does not take much to satisfy man when he is arrogant. He believes he has explained a phenomenon when he has made a mechanical model or found a group of mathematical formulae that enable him to foresee his own reactions at the end of a determined time. His laws are always *a posteriori.* They generally plunge him into depths of admiration. *A law is then essentially a product of the human brain and possesses no significance outside of man.* It exists only when it is formulated by him and if a law does not apply in every case, it is wrong; facts are always right. The difference between scientific and civil law is at once apparent. Civil law is "a rule established so that an intelligent being can be guided by an intelligent being who wields power over him." (Clifford). Their only character in common is that both are a product of

118

the human brain, *and the universal value of the laws of nature only has significance as long as we have reference to a certain type of perceptive faculty, namely, to that of the normal human being.*

One of the objections the reader will certainly be tempted to make is the following: "You will nevertheless admit that the law of gravitation existed before the birth of Newton." To which we will simply reply: "Newton's law certainly did not exist, *in the form he gave it.*" This law is not so much the discovery by Newton of a rule determining the movements of the planets, as the invention of a method, based on uncontrollable hypotheses which enable us to briefly describe the succession of sensorial impressions that we call the planetary movements. That is what Pearson calls "mental stenography." Certainly the celestial bodies evolved similarly in time and in space for Ptolemy and for Newton; they did not change for Einstein who nevertheless "interpreted" what he saw in a different way. This evolution is coupled with that of the entire universe. It is more than a hundred million light years in diameter and is perhaps only a minute bubble in "something" infinitely more vast, and it has nothing much in common with our little human law which covers a relatively very short period of a few million years in the history of the universe. Who can affirm that this law, or any other, will still be valid in a hundred thousand million years?

Thus Newton's genial law is almost static, and for man, the receiver, it represents the aspect of a relatively immobilized infinitesimal section of the phenomenon. We cannot infer from it the history of the worlds any more than we can reconstitute the whole story contained in two thousand feet of film by examining one single frame. When we speak of a "relatively immobilized section" we mean that the lapse of time considered is too short with respect to the immense periods of evolution of the worlds for the laws of the latter to be accessible to us. The study under a microscope of a fragment of film would certainly teach us many interesting things. So would its chemical analysis. We could build a whole science on these foundations but it would be without any true relation to the evolution of the *events* registered on the whole film, which only acquire a reality in our eyes as a result of the unwinding at a certain speed in the projector. Once again, this matters little. We will never know anything but our laws, those which govern the succession of our impressions, that is to say, of our universe. Let us therefore cease to distress ourselves because of their relativity, and let us see what methods we use to establish them. The result will be more useful than the pursuit of the illusion of absolute reality.

The general scientific method is the experimental method based, on the one hand, on the observation of phenomena and on the other hand, on deduction and analysis. The analytical method is evidently the only one that enables us to satisfy the curiosity which characterizes us and which is responsible for the intellectual evolution of man. We find this method everywhere: in art, sociology, literature, or science. In order to know we must analyze. In the first three manifestations of human activity cited above, analysis is often reinforced by intuition. But intuition is not really a method, for it is doubtful whether it can be acquired or even perfected under normal conditions in our actual civilization. It is a gift that is unequally distributed. On the contrary, we use analysis whenever our curiosity or our interest leads us to seek the "how" of things. The child who breaks his engine with the aim of learning how it functions applies the same analytical method as the chemist, the physicist, and the biologist.

The question now arises as to whether this admirable tool, advocated by Descartes can, by itself give us the longed for answer in all cases. First of all, on what does our confidence in the value of analysis rest? It must be admitted that the extension and prestige of this method are relatively recent. It was occasionally, but not systematically employed before Bacon, Descartes, and Pascal. Experimental science—with the exception of the great alchemists and a few brilliant minds of the seven teenth century—was born in the eighteenth century.

Pascal is an illustrious example of this transitory period. A mathematical genius who, we are told, rediscovered the first propositions of Euclid's geometry when he was twelve years old and who at sixteen wrote a treatise on conic sections which astonished Descartes. He achieved this intuitively, inductively, and not by applying the analytical, experimental method. But it was partly due to this last method that he resolved the problems relating to the equilibrium of liquids and the weight of air.

Like children we are irresistibly drawn by our curiosity to pull apart and analyze, and our confidence in this method seems essentially based on a belief in the fundamental simplicity of things and in the possibility of explaining the complex by adding up simple factors or elements. In the vast majority of cases, this point of view is certainly justified. We dissect phenomena instinctively in the hope of reaching the simpler ones which composed them. Our ambition is fully satisfied when having achieved this goal, we succeed in reconstituting the initial phenomenon through synthesis. Faced by the immense complication of the universe, it was very tempting to imagine that one day we would be able to understand and explain everything by means of a small number of elements and fundamental laws. People even went so far as to consider the simplicity of a theory or a hypothesis as a proof of its value. Since 1900, and especially in the last ten years, facts have taken it upon themselves to cure us of this naivety. But we still suffer today from the errors which pushed certain philosophers and some scientists on to the path of hasty generalizations and premature extrapolations.

This illusion of simplicity is worth developing more closely. The study of analytical reasoning will give us the occasion to do so. To avoid the dryness of a dissertation, we will discuss examples and try to show that analysis is efficacious and sure between certain well defined limits, but that in the majority of cases it ceases to furnish useful information as soon as it is carried beyond a certain threshold. This threshold is easily crossed in one direction but not in the opposite direction, namely in the direction of synthesis. We will shortly see that it is this threshold which constitutes the clearest demarcation line between the different human sciences.

Let us begin arbitrarily, not with the most complex science (sociology) nor with the simplest (physics) but with the most captivating sciences—

those dealing with man. They are the most fundamental ones for us. To know the nature of physical man, we must analyze it. One of the first stages will be dissection. Anatomy, a descriptive contemplative science, according to Claude Bernard's expression, teaches us the details of our internal structure. It enables us to isolate the organs, the muscles, the bones, and the nerves. The topographical classification it establishes is useful to serialize the questions but is, nevertheless, superficial, for though the functions of the organs are tied to their structural aspect, we know that no organ functions independently of the others. The human body constitutes an admirable synthesis; a harmonious whole where everything is linked and where everything contributes either in a known or an unknown way to the equilibrium of the whole. In the simplest form of analysis—dissection—we are already faced with other problems that are no longer man as a whole but fragments of man; dead fragments. Professor Widal, and other great doctors, understood this fact and urged their pupils to interest themselves above all in the clinical study of a patient. The superiority of French medicine is due to the observance of this rule.

It is true that we can study without first killing. Experiments *in vivo* are the basis of the fundamental science of physiology. The functions of each organ in respect to others are considered in this science. Thanks to anatomy, which has given us beforehand the detailed plan of the factory, if I may use this expression, we try to seize and understand the mechanisms by which the air we breathe and our daily food transform themselves into work, heat, muscles, bone, blood, and all kinds of hormones. That is how we learned the general chemical, physical, and physicochemical conditions of life, and how we came to understand the processes of the phenomena of nutrition in their immense complexity; of respiration and the maintenance of animal heat, of circulation, of internal and external secretions, and finally, of the phenomena of the excitation of living matter and of the nervous system.

Anatomists, histologists, and in their wake, physiologists, forced by the necessity of passing from the complex to the simple, arrived at the

cells; the constituent elements of the organs. An important chapter of biology, cytology, is given over to this study. We have already described Carrel's remarkable methods. One of the most outstanding results of his experiments was the revelation that, besides the static cytology, a cytologic physiology, based on the conservation of living cells, should be erected.

Being thus in possession of the ultimate element of the living being, an element which keeps its personality if it is cultivated under proper conditions, we could pride ourselves rightly on the success of the analytical method. We had attained a great simplification; *but this result was only achieved at the price of abandoning certain problems, and their consideration remained fundamental for the comprehension of the being as a whole.* For, as we have already stated, when we isolate an organ or a fragment of tissue, we eliminate the possibility of studying the relations existing between this organ and the other organs, and these relations, as we know, often condition its functioning. By being thus simplified, the problems were not solved—*they were replaced by others.* We know the multiple cells of the vegetable or animal organism, but what has become of the grace of the flower, of its colors and perfumes destined

123

to perpetuate the species through the intermediary of insects? What has become of the song of the bird, of the intelligence of man? In order to study the harmonious development of beings and the relation between parts, it is necessary not to oversimplify. Normal conditions cannot be brushed aside with impunity, if one seeks to characterize the whole. It is difficult nowadays to know what influence a certain distant endocrine gland can have on such and such a physiological function which is apparently independent and above all to know the part played by the nervous system. Just recently, Carrel, with the help of Lindbergh for the material realization, has perfected a technique which represents a considerable progress in this direction.

Analysis does not allow us to synthesize by giving us the structural element; the cell. Without knowing it we are led away from our point of departure, and we do not know at what moment we lose sight of the details—admitting that they are discernable—that could have enlightened us on the fundamental coordination. To study the latter we must go back, and the advantage gained by the knowledge of the isolated cells is in general no longer of great help. Without being aware of it we have passed a threshold which separates us from the global problem.

But we do not stop there and our appetite for analysis is far from sated. The stomach, the liver, the pancreas, and the glands digest—namely decompose and secrete—namely manufacture—quantities of substances. New cells are born. A tremendous, incessant biological and chemical activity resides in the cells. To reach it we dissociate them, and the reacting bodies are extracted. Our methods have enabled us to seize and explain a great number of reactions; not those that build, but those that destroy. The phenomena of combustion and digestion are familiar. We follow the disintegration of the albuminoid substances (the proteids or proteins), in one word, their simplification, but we do not yet know how they synthesize. It is always easier to demolish than to build. And when we build, when by synthesis we succeed at the price of a thousand difficulties, in reproducing one of the substances manufactured by our cells (a hormone, adrenalin, or thyroxine, for example), we know that our methods are far clumsier and less perfect than those employed by the cells of the suprarenal glands and the thyroid gland. We imitate the production of these prodigious, microscopic laboratories very well, but our science of today is limited to this imitation. We cannot reconstitute the laboratory itself, and we are ignorant of its methods.

As soon as we reach this stage of chemical analysis, we completely lose contact with life. Once more we have crossed, with the greatest ease, a threshold that we cannot pass in the opposite direction. Carried away by our need to know we deliberately turn our backs on the integral problem that we meant to sift. We apply all the resources of our techniques and of our intelligence to the study of this substratum of living matter—the protein molecule. Here we fall quickly. We know that this protein is constituted of simple elements, the proteoses, themselves resolvable into polypeptides and finally into aminoacids which are decomposed into well—defined chemical groups. We also know that when analyzing a protein we lose none of the elements of this extraordinarily complicated body which comprises several thousand atoms, and that we recover them all in weight at the end of the experiment. We know therefore that we end by possessing all the bricks of the edifice, but we also know that as soon as we begin to demolish it, to analyze it, we irremediably destroy something which cannot be weighed, nor titrated, and which characterized the whole edifice. This is a new threshold; we go down another small step. And when we look back we are astonished to discover that an impassable wall has arisen behind us. Every time we touch this molecule we suppress one or more biological properties. Where did they come from? Not from one of its chemical constituents but probably from the position of the latter in the structure composed of all the adjoining elements. To give an idea of the coordination of the whole we need only say that if two of the approximately eight thousand atoms that constitute one of these molecules are disposed in a rigorously defined way and can be pivoted and substituted one for the other, certain biological properties of the entire molecule are completely modified. The experiment, made possible by the magnificent work of Karl Landsteiner, was realized by Avery and Goebel at the Rockefeller Institute.

Thus, when the analysis is finished, only a certain quantity of carbon, hydrogen, oxygen, nitrogen, and sometimes a trace of sulphur, phosphorus, or iron, remains in the test tubes. These bodies, identical to those of mineral chemistry, can be exactly titrated. But what has become of the marvelous little factory, the workings of which we had meant to study? We are left with only pure inert products that could have been bought by the pound anywhere.

How do the cells work? Is there an intermediary stage which escapes us? At what moment? And finally what is the meaning of the precision of our experiments? The answer is easy.

The precision we have attained belongs to *another* problem. At a given moment we destroyed our principal problem. We do not know how or when, and we were not even aware of it. We readily allow ourselves to glide on a kind of toboggan without realizing that it cannot help us to make the return ascent. At the present time, we do not even see any way of linking the acquired results to the main problem. We can merely note that living beings are composed of materials which, although essentially

constituted of the same elements as the inorganic bodies, are endowed by their dimension and their structure in space, with special properties that cannot be inferred from those of their common elements. We perceive these qualities without understanding them, and they characterize all living matter. Every simplification results in a greater stability but, at the same time, in the loss of a characteristic quality which was linked to the initial fragility. The combinations introduced by life are not special in themselves, but it is from their complexity that their vital properties are derived. And just as the beauty and the value of a Rembrandt painting cannot be appreciated by chemically analyzing the colors spread out on the canvas, so for a long time yet chemical methods will not furnish the answers to the important questions propounded by the biologists.

And that is what could be called the illusion of reasoning or the illusion of simplicity. It applies, moreover, from the top to the bottom of the ladder. It could be easily demonstrated that the threshold of chemistry is passed when the structure of the atom is attained. We are far from being able to predict the physical properties of a simple body from the number of electrons which revolve around its nucleus, yet, as we saw at the beginning of this article, these qualities constitute its reality with respect to ourselves. We therefore cannot foresee the sensory reaction it will determine in us; will it be a gas, a liquid, or a solid at the ordinary temperature? What we know belongs to the intellectual, speculative realm and not as yet to the real realm. We do not even know how the combination of two gases like hydrogen and oxygen creates water—that compound with such curious properties to which we pay no attention simply because, as Montaigne said, "familiarity dulls perception." When we cross the threshold of the molecule, or rather of the aggregation of molecules, we enter a realm that is different from the chemistry and the physics of our tangible world. We penetrate into the world of photons and electrons; of electric particles; of light particles. It is a real world without doubt, but it is not directly perceptible nor translatable. A hiatus exists between the two, just as it exists between the chemistry of inorganic bodies and that of living matter; between the latter and the protoplasm; between the protoplasm and the cell; between the cell and the organ; between the organ and the individual. At the summit—man. To say that man is ultimately an assemblage of positive nuclei and electrons is not a false statement, but it is so incomplete that it is worthless. Analysis can give no other answer. It therefore does not see everything.

If we complicate the problem still further by going beyond man and considering him as an element of society, we reach another threshold. Sociology cannot be studied by means of an isolated man. Here it is man himself who becomes the indivisible unit beyond which the sociological problem ceases to exist as the biological problem disappears beyond the cell. Thus every science is limited and characterized by a threshold, an indivisible unit beyond which analysis is no longer able to bring an answer to the question asked but leads us insensibly into another domain.

Behind these tiers, which are the proof of the inadequacy of our brain and the stigma of our human condition, we see, or rather surmise, the harmonious concatenation of the universe which escapes us—the objective universe. We like to think that a continuous and absolute relation exists between the simple hydrogen atom with one electron, between even this electron and the Milky Way, between our Milky Way and the others, the nebula Berenice's Hair (Coma Berenices) for instance, whose light takes fifty million years to reach us, from the infinitely small to the infinitely great, passing through our humble individual. This is a purely anthropomorphic hypothesis. Its origin can easily be traced to the succession of reactions and the ideas determined in us by the universe such as it is revealed to us by our senses. We here skirt metaphysics, and we evade reality. We can see, in spite of ourselves, that this illusion of our reasoning can lead us far from the path we had decided to follow. It suffices to be warned in order not to be duped and to avoid the grave error of denying the existence of what we do not see. A famous doctor, victim of this illusion and perhaps also of an immoderate confidence in human science, once said : "The soul? I have never touched it with my scalpel." Nobody doubted it. But neither would the voice of Caruso be heard on a record if we treated it in the same way. We cannot reproach this skeptic for having made a declaration of faith, which was his unquestioned right; nor for choosing the materialistic thesis, which at that time enjoyed a prestige in intellectual circles, which was solidly based on the most enviable ignorance and optimism. We can, however, reproach him for pronouncing futile words to which the ill-informed public, deceived by the authority attached to his name, attributed the importance of a scientific proof.

Analysis, then, keeps all its value as long as we do not use it beyond the characteristic threshold represented in the different sciences by the indivisible unity with which its objects are built. So as not to make an involuntary error beyond this limit, it is important to remember that the threshold was crossed, and that the conclusions derived from experimental facts garnered on the other side of this threshold can in no case be legitimately applied to those on this side. The nonobservance of this rule has itself raised many false problems and led to many conflicts.

So many other sources of error exist that they cannot all be examined. Nevertheless, there are two which by their importance seem to merit our attention. One of these could be called "the illusion of thermodynamics—the other "the illusion of causality." We apologize for being obliged to employ terms that may seem rather forbidding. The reader is aware of the fact that modern philosophy rests in part on experimental science. If we seek to criticize it, we must therefore have recourse to the consecrated terminology which has the advantage of being brief and precise.

Thermodynamics, or energetics, owes its name to the fact that this fundamental branch of science has established the laws which govern the transformation of energy into heat and vice versa. The first law of thermodynamics teaches us that although energy takes on multiple aspects —kinetic, thermic, chemical, electric, etc.—and can be converted from one form to another, there is never any loss or gain during the transformation. It is the law of the conservation of energy. For example, the chemical energy brought into play by the explosion of the powder in a cannon is transformed into heat and movement. When the shell is projected (kinetic energy) and comes into contact with armor plate which stops it, there is such an abrupt rise in temperature that the steel can melt. When brakes are used to stop a fast-moving car, they become heated. The heat disengaged by the combustion of coal puts a steam engine in motion; the chemical energy of an electric battery turns a motor, and reciprocally a waterfall acting on a dynamo produces electric energy that can be used to charge the batteries to heat water or to electrolyze a solution so as to nickel plate or gild an object.

The second law of thermodynamics or Carnot-Clausius law is a little more abstract. It deals with the quantitative relations which *restrain* the convertibility of energy. It establishes that, although a work or the kinetic energy of a body in movement can transform itself in different ways and be finally converted into heat, the reverse evolution, from heat into work, is possible only *under certain conditions*. In other words, when it is transformed into heat, energy is definitely lowered. A certain quantity of heat can always pass from a hot body to a body that is colder —even when accomplishing a work—but it is impossible to make even a minimum quantity of heat pass from a body that is colder to a hotter body without using work from the exterior. In cooling this body has lost not only a certain quantity of heat but also certain qualities; half a liter of water at 100° C. will boil an egg, but water at 50° C. will never accomplish this, no matter how great the quantity. If energy conserves itself the *utilizable value* of this energy decreases every time there has been a transformation into heat and the higher the temperature, the greater is this value.

This law is absolutely universal. We know of no exception in the organized world, in the domain where our statistical laws reign. It is a principle. It brings about consequences the importance of which is absolutely general but on which we cannot dwell here. We will merely say that it is the most solid foundation of our modern science, the indispensible Ariadne's clue. The preceding lines explain why thermodynamics is considered as the common framework of all the physical, chemical, and mechanical sciences.

In his book *Physico Chemical Evolution* Charles Guye brilliantly sets forth an impressive series of reasons, which lead to the conclusion that the high efficiency of "living machines" rules out the hypothesis that they are thermic machines. On the other hand, we are led to question, with Lord Kelvin and Helmholtz, whether living organisms obey the Carnot-Clausius law. This short seemingly inoffensive statement, more revolutionary than was the theory of Copernicus in his time, is accepted today by the most distinguished minds who are, nevertheless, careful not to comment on it except by a shake of the head. It signifies that the burning question—is there a basic difference between inanimate inorganic bodies and living beings?—can and should be raised again today. If such a basic difference exists we must abandon the hope of explaining the appearance and persistence of life by means of our actual science, and it no longer suffices to invoke scientific laws, no matter how they are expressed, to banish all finalism from the evolution of life.

Two possibilities exist: either we verify the laws governing inert matter in *all* phenomena and in all biological reactions when we study them quantitatively, or else we do not verify them—or at least, not always.

131

In the first case, there is no reason for the secret of life itself not to be unveiled one day. In the second case, it is impossible to be as affirmative. It is certain that at present we find ourselves in the second alternative. All physiologists are in accord on this subject. We are thus led by science and in complete liberty of thought to admit the contrary of what had been rather lightly postulated by some philosophic schools. After a long detour, we have now been brought back to Pascal's wager [1] but with some unexpected additional arguments which would have delighted that great mind.

We will now briefly evoke the last illusion, the one of causality which is rather subtle and particularly serious.

Physics has undergone profound upheavals in the last few years. The realm of the physicist resembles a country ravaged by a series of earthquakes and tidal waves. Let us leave aside the material details, the experimental facts which have obliged the scientist to completely modify the idea he had of the nature of things and of the universe, and let us examine the results which have brought about important changes in the relations between phenomena or, more exactly, in our interpretation of their sequence, of their evolution. All our classical science rests on the notion of *determinism*. We say that a phenomenon is well known when we have succeeded in establishing the factors which determine its appearance. The less unknown factors there are, and the better we can link it to a posterior phenomenon of which it is the cause, the more it interests us. We therefore try to establish the concatenation of the successive causal relations; and to consider each fact, not so much for itself but as an intermediary between its cause and effect. The goal of research, as we stated above, is the study of the relations between phenomena. Our blind belief in an absolute determinism was for a long time at the base of our confidence in science. But this determinism underwent a profound evolution at the beginning of the century with Boltzmann. Our physical laws were transformed into *statistical* laws the accuracy

[1] *Les Pensées*, Ist Ed. (Paris, Desprez, 1670), chap. VII, p. 55.

of which depends on the enormous number of elements present. The greater this number the greater the increase in precision; the smaller it is, the more the precision decreases. Below a certain value, the laws no longer apply. Moreover, the statistic results are the only ones accessible to our determinations [1].

We therefore do not often find ourselves faced with phenomena that depend on a small number of elements, *except in living organisms.* Following the statistical concept based on the law of large numbers by Gauss, a phenomenon, instead of being rigidly determined, is now only considered as *extremely probable.* This mathematical probability is, moreover, so great that it is practically a certainty. Nothing is changed therefore except that the concept of causality has become more supple. But the principle of indeterminacy, introduced in 1927 by Professor Heisenberg, is now completely incorporated into undulatory mechanics. Its importance can be compared with that of the theory of relativity or

---

[1] A simple example will elucidate the preceding sentence: a physical law states that if two gases at different pressures are contained in two vessels communicating with each other by a stopcock, the pressure will become equal as soon as the latter is opened. Common sense indicates this. Thermodynamics explains a certain state of equilibrium which is attained when the pressures are equalized. The pressure of gas is due to the shocks of the molecules against the walls of the container. It is therefore proportional to their number. This number being always very great—one cubic centimeter, a little less than a thimble, contains about thirty thousand million billion gas molecules. It is unimportant if the number is not exactly equal. A few million more in one container than in the other will never introduce a measurable difference in the pressure; a difference of one per thousand would represent a divergence of several million billion molecules in vessels of one cubic centimeter. Hence the name of statistical law or law of large numbers. The accessible measurable phenomenon, the pressure, is the statistical resultant of the individual actions. The kinetic theory and thermodynamics explain it satisfactorily. But if the volume of the vessels were reduced to the point where they contain only ten molecules each, the passage of one molecule through the aperture would determine a difference of ten percent in the pressure, and the law of equality of pressure will be false; thermodynamics will be wrong. If only two molecules were present, the difference would be one hundred percent; only the unknown laws that govern the movements of the individual molecule would enter into play and there would no longer be any pressure so to speak, but only a shock. In organized beings not only do we find cells that are already small, but they contain structural elements that play a well-defined role, and their dimensions are such that the molecules are in very small numbers causing fluctuations to become preponderant. We have already developed this idea in the *Revue de Paris,* Jan. 15. 1929.

with the works of Louis de Broglie. This principle demonstrates that we can never know *all* the elements (position and velocity) necessary in order to foresee exactly the future action of one of the ultimate elements; photon or electron. We can know one half (position *or* velocity) but not the two together because the observation itself influences the movement. It is not a question of ignorance, but of a necessary limitation. Consequently, we actually only dispose of statistical, global laws, and furthermore, we are *forbidden* to hope that we will discover one day the laws that govern the elementary particles and which, theoretically, would alone enable us to rigorously foresee the future and therefore be absolute laws.

Now, a statistical law is only valid if its elementary particles are entirely governed by chance. If this were not the case, if directed events were produced, we would observe fluctuations more or less frequently but always in the same direction, and our law would be affected by this disturbing element. Let us take an example.The success of insurance companies is possible because it is admitted that a comparable number of accidents will happen every year — the number of the accidents is known fairly accurately by previous statistics. This is our law. It is sufficiently precise for the shareholders to be paid dividends. But if an arsonist systematically starts fires — i.e. if an element no longer due to chance but to malevolence enters into play — there will be such a fluctuation that the company will be bankrupt. This crude example enables one to understand not only the meaning we give to the word chance but also the nature of the precision attained. Indeed, if a company bases its calculations on a number of approximately constant fires for a period of five years, for example, and succeeds easily in foreseeing *how many* houses will be destroyed yearly, it is, on the other hand, incapable of knowing beforehand *which* houses will burn.

Thus, in the inorganic world everything takes place as if chance alone, the totally disordered movement, entered into play. But then, whence comes the regularity, the harmony, the continuity — in a word, the evolution of living beings? Following an example given by Guye we can conceive, if need be, that a marvelous optical instrument like the eye could have been built once. But it is more difficult to admit that this construction succeeds at the first attempt, not only in the organism considered but also in all the living beings that constitute its numberless progeny. As long as Heisenberg's principle was not established, it was hoped that the statistical form we had given our laws was only momentary and that by studying the individual actions of the elementary particles, future geniuses would one day establish laws that would shed a new light on this evolution which we discern. Today we know that this is forbidden for reasons that do not depend on our intelligence but on our structure and on the structure we attribute to the universe. The hazard inherent in the analytical method criticized above, reappears. We cannot conceive a science that is not based on our modes of thought, and this brings us to within an ace of an absolute limitation innate in us and in themselves. We are condemned to remain in this vicious circle as long as we only have recourse to the experimental scientific method on which we rightly pride ourselves. Does this mean that another purely intuitive method would enable us to more fully understand the ultimate mechanism and the meaning of our universe? It is premature to affirm this.

The fact that the progress of science has reached a stage where a revision of certain concepts is essential has, I hope, been sufficiently demonstrated. These concepts, derived from generous but imprudent extrapolations, have insensibly become dogma with age. The truth of today is no longer that of yesterday. It has not changed, but its aspect has been modified for us in a way that was unforeseen by our predecessors, just as a landscape changes its aspect for a near-sighted person when he puts on his glasses. For the encyclopedists it appeared from afar like a presumably marvelous statue at the end of a verdant and obscure path in a park filled with mystery but seemingly easy of access. This was the origin of the misunderstanding from which we still suffer. The philosophers had such a need of clarity and liberty; they were so intoxicated with the successes of human intelligence that they could not differentiate between what they really saw and what they wished to see. Without knowing it they always slightly overstepped the boundary drawn by scientific rigor. The scientists in the laboratory gathered and carefully classified facts, while philosophers built theories and did not realize that they were straying farther and farther from that truth which, without their being aware of it, had seduced them; more as a weapon against obscurantism and religious authority than by its sole arid beauty.

On the other hand, as everything is only illusion, how can we be surprised that men wanted to lean in first analysis on that which is most real but also most mysterious in us; our anxiety? We are ignorant of the world itself. We only know it through human reactions. Our only reality springs from inside ourselves. There is no specific difference between the collective hallucination of a group of spectators on whom a Hindu fakir imposes certain sensory impressions — the sight of a child who climbs a rope thrown into the air and then suddenly disappears — and that other collective hallucination which we call our science. We refuse to believe in miracles. Be it so. But what do we call a miracle? An event that our science cannot explain? In that case we are surrounded — submerged by miracles. On the other hand, it can be argued that a great many have already been explained, and that we will progressively explain all the others. This is not proved, for the fact that we have explained them would prove that they were not miracles. In general, however, we do not explain but only displace them. And today our science, betraying its sponsors but not its disciples, demonstrates that we are forbidden to go beyond a certain limit. But even if all other miracles were disposed of there would always be the "fillip" for which Pascal could not forgive Descartes.

Finally, we are often victims of the illusion of words. How many obscurities, for instance, are hidden in the word "evolution," a term so impressive that it overshadows everything? Let us remember the deep and ironical words of W. K. Chesterton: the word 'evolution' has an unfortunate tendency to substitute itself for the word 'explanation' and many people consider that it releases them from thinking further, just as they live under the vague illusion that they have read *The Origin of Species*. This confusion arises from the fallacious idea of a slow transition like the imperceptible rise of a river. Furthermore, it is illogical, seeing that greater or less rapidity has nothing to do with it and that Mr. Homais is just as apt to be flabbergasted by a slow miracle as by a sudden miracle. Historical materialism does not seem to be able to rid itself of the curious error that a difficulty is turned, even resolved, if everything is blamed on time."

There are many other illusions. There will always be some. What does it matter? What counts is life as it is and not as we would like it to be. Never, in the whole history of the world, have we approached as closely the mysteries which surround us; never have we so well understood the immensity of our ignorance and of our pride. The last pages of *The Mysterious Universe* by Sir James Jeans should be read so as to understand how meager, from the point of view of certitude, are the benefits we have derived from our efforts. But who, in science is preoccupied with benefits? The cry of Du Bois-Reymond —"Ignorabimus"— is only heartbreaking for those who want to make of science a tool and not a goal. At our present stage it would take dozens of centuries to elucidate not all the problems but only those that we have asked ourselves so far. The future appears rich in magnificent hopes if we stay within our intellectual domain without trying to encroach on the others. The crisis in determinism of which we briefly spoke above, must be greeted as a progress, even if some very brilliant minds were truly grieved by it. Let us remember the pathetic appeal of one of the greatest physicists of our times, Professor Lorentz, at the Solvay Congress in 1927. "Could we not," he implored, "preserve determinism, *if only as a belief?*"

Science is not and never will be bankrupt as long as it deals only with its own subjects. It must not be asked to demonstrate when it can only describe. Many foolish statements would thus be avoided, and science would no longer be obliged to resolve difficulties which are unrelated to it and which only prove to what degree man needs a strong moral discipline so as not to mistake his passions for his reason.

OUR UNIVERSE AND ITS IMAGE 1939

Just as there are two different ways of using a funnel, so there are two ways of practicing science. If, as is customary, the liquid is poured into a bottle through the wide mouth, it will be reduced to a thin trickle when it comes out at the other end. The result will be entirely different if the liquid is poured into the small end. Likewise, in science we can start from a rather vast problem and by using the analytical method gradually reduce it to its elements. We can then choose one of these elements, reduce it to its constituent parts, and proceed in like manner until the time when the lack of credits, time, or collaborators force us to stop, sit down, and look around us.

But, even under the best possible conditions, it is never possible to go beyond a certain stage — there is a barrier that is impassable by definition. It is the barrier that limits the meadow where those children of our brain, the corpuscles, electrons, protons, neutrons, etc. — only known to us by their effects on another scale of observation — disport themselves in liberty.

When we act in the reverse order, as in the case of the funnel, we start from a special phenomenon and rise to the more general phenomenon of which it is only a constituent part. Here the task becomes difficult. Up to a certain point we remain in the scientific realm, but if we imperceptibly venture out too far, we run the risk of being swept away by the ebb on to the high seas of philosophy, like the fisherman who lets the hour of the rising tide go by. This has no drawbacks for a good sailor, but a fisherman is not perforce a good sailor and neither is a scientist necessarily a good philosopher.

On the other hand, the temptation is strong. The sea is calm and alluring and the curiosity of certain men is infinite. It is only by going out to sea that we can hope to obtain a general view of the harbor and then of the coast. And those who went out and were able to return brought back such marvelous and often such improbable accounts that they awakened our desire to verify their stories. Thirty years ago or more, towards the end of the nineteenth century, the current was clearly positivist — materialistic. The interpretations of Boltzmann were accepted with reservations and had not yet endangered the old determinism of Laplace. No one could foresee wave mechanics nor the principle of indeterminacy, save perhaps a few pure philosophers like Bergson.

Lately, however, this current seems to manifest a tendency to change its direction. The modern scientist of good faith — I am speaking of the one who thinks — can no longer retain this tranquil assurance which rests on a conviction. The new facts, instead of reinforcing this conviction have, on the contrary, shaken it. Philosophical doubt, which had in many cases replaced faith, has itself been replaced by a materialistic faith, and now the first gleam of a new philosophical doubt can be distinguished in scientific circles, especially in those of foreign countries. It is based on the recent discoveries relating to the nature of matter, the nature of life, and the inadequacy of the existing theories. We perceive that after having accumulated facts in order to erect theories, some people had come to the point where facts interested them only when they could support these theories. They do not always make a conscious choice. But even in a law court a perfectly honest witness who does not wish to hide anything makes a choice amongst his memories. If, for instance, he is asked to describe all his acts on a certain morning, he will say: "I got up at eight o'clock, I had breakfast, I went out, I took a No. 43 bus, I arrived at my office,..." He will not say: "I knocked my knee getting out of bed, I cut myself while shaving, I spilt a little coffee,

I turned around in the street to watch a pretty woman who was passing..." He deems these details irrelevant to the event on which he is being questioned. Therefore he makes an unconscious selection. In the same way, the scientist chooses the facts he considers significant and neglects the others. Only a genius can sometimes discover amongst the latter the element which will put him on the road to a great discovery. It is even because of this fact that the world will generally recognize, much later, that he has — or, alas had — genius.

If, then, instead of studying more and more limited phenomena, if instead of analyzing *ad infinitum*, with the aim of accumulating experimental facts, we elevate our minds by a superhuman effort and consider the entire universe as a single, complex phenomenon in which all other phenomena are integrated, we are led to separate in thought the three elements that condition our consciousness:

1. The objective origin of our reactions, namely, the phenomena that are external to us (independent of any hypothesis on the subject of their existence or nonexistence).

2. The direct reactions of our nervous system to these causes, i.e., our sensations.

3. The abstract thought that utilizes these purely qualitative materials to translate them into a purely quantitative language; the language of ratios.

It is this third element that constitutes the very framework of our science, which is inconceivable without it. For science is not born from the simple confrontation of the self with the universe. Science is the result of the replacement of all qualitative values — the only ones that are direct and indisputable — by quantitative values, numbers, or symbols expressing ratios. Yellow light becomes a wave length of 0.589μ.

All the sciences, all philosophies based on science, attempt to explain the universe by means of numbers and logical systems that are products of the human brain. While admitting that it is difficult to conceive another method, it must, nevertheless, be recognized that only an unshakable

141

optimism can give us the hope of obtaining perfect agreement and an answer to all the questions. We can debate whether such an optimism is a quality or an infirmity. No matter what is said or done, there is no common measure between quality and the number; for quality is a direct value which depends solely on our sense organs, that are necessary and sufficient, and on our consciousness. On the other hand, the number can only express a ratio, a measurement — which could be obtained independently of almost the entire sensorial system on condition that a single sensitive point existed in our retina, even if this point only reacted to light and darkness without distinguishing colors. We can, indeed, reduce all experimental controls to the coincidence of two lines.

The image of the world furnished by our senses may therefore be very different from the reality, but this observation is completely deprived of significance inasmuch as this image constitutes *all* our reality. Science does not even provide an image of the universe; it provides methods which enable us to calculate numbers, empirically related to our sensorial images and thanks to which, after another translation, we can foresee the evolution of these subjective images in time. It also provides us with a coherent diagram of the sequence which probably expresses the attendant relations of certain objective relations between the phenomena outside ourselves, as Jean Mariani believes.

To neglect consciousness is, strictly speaking, not to interest oneself in the universe in so far as it is a global phenomenon. In this immense phenomenon the most significant fact for man is human consciousness, without which the cosmos would not exist for him. Our universe is therefore conditioned by a phenomenon which is perhaps not more vast but to which it owes its grandeur and its very existence. When we speak of the universe and try to catch a glimpse of its evolution, we therefore do not have the right to eliminate consciousness not only as an element of the whole but also as a witness and a result of this evolution. Indeed it is probable, or at least possible, that human intelligence is the result of the slow adaptation of life to its environment. If we admit that it is the product of this long process, we must also

admit that a very close relation exists between it and the universe. But every time we try to separate these two aspects of evolution, we may be certain of committing errors comparable to and even greater than those revealed by Einstein in his theory of restricted relativity. I think everyone will agree on this if it is discussed in good faith. But modern "philosophic" literature is a permanent source of surprise as the most celebrated authors constantly seem 'to lose sight of these simple truths known even before Kant. Far be it from me to doubt their honesty. But they reason like the old stagehand, who never having sat with the audience, nevertheless had very decided views on the theatrical production of his time and would not brook any discussion. His opinion was based solely on the changes of scenery, on what was feasible, and on the lighting effects. He judged severely the authors who did not utilize the play of lights or who required only one set of scenery for three acts. Strangely enough he was sometimes right, for he deeply admired the way in which Shakespeare is represented today. The idea that a play could be judged from the other side of the curtain seemed to him comical, and although he spoke of the public with a condescending indulgence, he had nothing but utter contempt for the critics.

This stagehand seems ridiculous to us, yet his point of view can be defended, as can the point of view of the critic who judges the play from what he sees and hears. They are, in short, two aspects of the same phenomenon, and we have a tendency to imitate the stagehand. I know that common sense is a quality that is out of date and often dangerous. But a minimum of common sense would seem to be useful when one attempts to reason. I cannot here review the errors of common sense which abound in the so-called scientific-philosophy, but I would like to cite a fundamental error that was pointed out by Whitehead with profound irony and a distinctly English sense of humor. Speaking of the application of physical and chemical notions to the problems of life, he says: "The brilliant success of this method is admitted, but you cannot limit a problem by reason of a method of attack. The problem is to understand the operations of an animal body. It is evident

144

that certain operations of certain animal bodies depend upon the foresight of an end and the purpose to attain it. It is no solution of the problem to ignore this evidence because other operations have been explained in terms of physical and chemical laws. The existence of a problem is not even acknowledged. It is vehemently denied. Many a scientist has patiently designed experiments for the *purpose* of substantiating his belief that animal operations are motivated by no purposes. He has perhaps spent his spare time in writing articles to prove that human beings are as other animals so that 'purpose' is a category irrelevant for the explanation of their bodily activities, his own activities included. *Scientists, animated by the purpose of proving that they are purposeless, constitute an interesting subject for study."*

Consciousness must then be conceived of as an integral part of any phenomenon, and it is only by an arbitrary act that we systematically suppress the subjective element of an event or of a succession of events or of reasoning. It may be protested that people today are no longer dupes of absolute objectivity, and that any student of philosophy knows full well that fundamentally he reasons only subjectively. But the subjective on which he believes he reasons, is limited to the role of a recorder, of something external. For him there is, on one side, a real universe, and on the other a real self, and he is taught that the image of the universe seen through the self and thanks to it, does not necessarily conform to "reality." Great care is taken not to define this "reality" for him. As a result he unconsciously derives a very vague, somewhat dualistic conception in which the self acquires a reality and an existence of its own which is independent of the external universe — or almost so. He does not realize that by isolating a phenomenon in order to study it, he effects a choice which already represents an arbitrary filtration and which narrows the problem and gives it a special aspect. This aspect is conditioned by his own consciousness and intelligence even before he has transformed it and translated it into a quantitative language. He does not realize that if the self is the consequence of the opposition of the subjective to the objective, the objective only has a meaning in so far as it is an inseparable element from the self. When a chemist conceives and executes a chemical operation, when he observes a reaction, the most important phenomenon is not the reaction itself, it is the combination of chemist plus reaction. It is this phenomenon that is directly linked to man's universe.

Indeed, on the one hand, there are the chemical or natural products, the physical means destined to accomplish the analysis or synthesis (heat, electric current) — the regulating, controling, measuring instruments which enable us to follow the reactions between ponderable substances. But on the other hand, there is the patient accumulation of empirical and theoretical rules, there is the work plan, the choice of substances, the order of succession in the experiments. Finally, and above all, there is the question which the chemist has asked himself. This question calls for an answer which, like a piece in a puzzle, will occupy a well determined place in the picture that has slowly been painted by generations of chemists. Of these two procedures — the one purely material, the other immaterial and speculative — who can say which is the most important? The question is without interest, for it is evident that they are again only two aspects of the same phenomenon and that the one cannot be conceived without the other. But all the same, there is on the side of the intellectual phenomenon the expression of a very mysterious continuity. I doubt whether the explanation of this continuity can be found solely in the human brain.

I took the example of the chemist because it spontaneously arose in my mind. But it is clear that the preceding sentences apply to science in general and even to the historical fact. I can hear the argument of the pure scientist: "All this has nothing to do with science. Subjectivity or objectivity are of no importance. What counts is to attain a better knowledge of our universe in order to understand it, to dominate it, and to utilize it. Ultimately, we will apply these acquired notions to man, who will then be fully known." This argument has an unquestionable practical value. But it does not change the fact that the other problem exists and has a much greater importance and generality. For, besides the fact that man has created science, he has conceived morality and is preoccupied with his role and his fate in the universe and even beyond. If the purely physiological preoccupations, common to him and to the animals, are put aside, it can even be said that, on an average, the interest he brings to moral, social, economic, artistic and, I add, spiritual problems, distinctly dominates by its importance his interest in scientific problems and in the theories that are only accessible to him by their utilitarian aspect. And strange to say, he not only wants to know, but it is essential for him not to be wrong. There exists a subtle difference between these two aspirations that is difficult to define but that is felt intuitively.

Charles Guye, unquestionably one of the most remarkable and original minds of our time, is I think the first physicist to point out the necessity of taking into account the intervention of man when studying phenomena. In 1919 he had already written: "We will only fully understand the significance of the physicochemical phenomenon when we know the relation which unites it to the vital and psychic phenomenon which can accompany it in the living organism." I further believe that on the statistical scale a phenomenon can only be wholly known if all the phenomena that accompany and follow perception in the organism are known. In other words, it seems to me that a parallel can be established between the whole; phenomenon, sensation, psychic reaction, and the "chain reactions" of chemistry. The parallel is crude, for in the chain reactions we deal only with chemical actions whereas in the whole, of which we are speaking, we are dealing with physical, chemical, physiological, and psychic actions. We seriously simplify the problem when, by reasoning, we isolate the first link of the chain, the phenomenon, and give it an individual existence, *even though this existence is merged in our brain with the last link which is the sensorial image.*

From our momentary human point of view, this can have no importance practically. If, on the contrary, we consider the event as contributing to the evolution of the entire universe, we obviously possess only an incomplete answer. For this reason, far from being forbidden it is desirable that we should occasionally consider problems that are more vast, more general — in other words, use the wrong side of the funnel. It is, henceforth, not only possible but necessary to examine philosophical problems scientifically. The recent developments of physics, from Einstein to Louis de Broglie and Heisenberg, have undoubtedly profoundly influenced our philosophy. A more piecemeal study of phenomena cannot by itself lead us very far, although it must continue. To isolate a phenomenon, we give it a beginning. Let us not be duped by this word. Every beginning denotes the end of something, and every end denotes a beginning; does not the agony of a being also have a beginning? Beginning and end are essentially human concepts and have no absolute meaning.

This is true of all the manifestations of human intelligence. Apparently man can think only by isolating events, more or less arbitrarily and artificially, and by cutting them up into slices. This fact is particularly striking in history. Indeed, is there anything more artificial than what is called "The History of France"? After having been amputated from almost all the external events which have determined and conditioned it, nothing remains but a parody on which successive historians, with few exceptions, have impressed the mark of their personality or of the passions and interests they serve. There is only one history; it is universal history, and every historical fact is linked by innumerable ramifications to all the earlier or contemporary historical facts in all the surrounding countries. When we consider it separately, it is as difficult to understand and to judge as it is to judge a Rembrandt painting by examining only a small square about the size of a postage stamp. And even if we study it through a magnifying glass, we will not increase our knowledge.

Our science tends to suppress continuity by granulating matter, electricity, and energy. In spite of all our efforts it nevertheless exists. Is not the very continuity of these efforts to destroy it a proof of its existence, an existence different from the simple statistical indetermination? One of the most perplexing problems man must face is that of the nature of this continuity, its reason for existence, and it is perhaps

148

the most important one. It may be that the solution will always escape us, and that by the very structure of our brain we here touch the limits of the knowable. The immense difficulty of our problem comes from the fact that we have reached a point where we try to explain the tool by means of the tool itself; thought by means of thought. We run up against a material impossibility which is not unlike that of a puppy who turns around and around, with increasing rapidity, in the vain hope of biting his tail. Or, to use a less trivial comparison, an impossibility of the same nature as the one that derives from the interaction of the observation and the phenomenon and which is at the base of the Heisenberg principle of indeterminacy. The fact that we know how to break up a phenomenon into discontinuous elements does not suppress continuity on another scale of observation. There is not a single phenomenon that is not the result of a continuity in time.

I have given a very brief summary of the purely rational problem of continuity. It is evident, that thus conceived it cannot be confused with the problem as propounded by pure physics which precisely neglects the element of "consciousness." For instance, Fürth asks himself in a recent article [1] whether in view of the differential equation or system of equations describing the variation of certain observable physical dimensions of a body, that are homogeneous in space and in time, it is possible to be satisfied by this continuous description, or whether a spacial or temporal structure should be made to intervene so as to obtain a better understanding of the phenomenon in question. It is clear that the equations are capable of properly representing the phenomenon if the material constants that figure in these equations can be interpreted with respect to their physical dimensions within the framework of a theory of continuity. In other words, if we respect the homogeneity of the elements of the problem, we obtain a valid and homogeneous answer. The question is purely formal, symbolic, and logical, but it does not attain the very nature of the relations between the continuous and the

---

[1] *Annalen der Physik* (1938).

discontinuous. We must not underestimate intuition, which imposes the idea of continuity upon us, for its roots are probably deeper than those of logic. The foundations of our science rest on this faith in continuity. We can admit, if need be, that the high probability foreseen by the increase in entropy can be practically taken for a certainty as far as the inorganic universe is concerned, and that this continuity is only a subjective aspect of this increase. But as soon as we penetrate into the organic world, we are in difficulty for we encounter an immense number of macroscopic phenomena that evolve following more or less lengthy periods, from a few hours (life of the microbes) up to millions of years (life and evolution of species—for example, insects). In the first—and even in the second—analysis they do not seem to be the exact expression of a probability. We would experience a certain difficulty if we had to express the probability that the evolution begun by the trilobites of the secondary period, or any other animal of any other period, would one day culminate in man with his brain. If we next had to express the probability that there would be two men and then millions, similar to the first

but nevertheless manifesting nonequivocal signs of progress, I think I can say without exaggeration, that we would be overwhelmed. We are brought back, imperceptibly, to Whitehead's argument, the most powerful ever given in favor of finalism.

By limiting his efforts to the reduction of phenomena into their constituent elements, man does not approach the important problems that interest him. Until lately, certain of these belonged more to the realm of philosophy than to that of science, but new light has been shed on them by the progress of modern physics. The human species has drawn from within itself the foundations of the theories which have made it possible to establish a coordination probably artificial but certainly useful, between a long series of phenomena.

It is evident, for example, that the evolution of the universe and the evolution of organic beings are questions of prime importance, and that the notion of entropy and the interpretations by Boltzmann have enabled us to consider them in an entirely new light. They have passed from the realm of pure speculation into the experimental realm. It is far from certain that the concept of entropy can apply to the evolution of life. The simple demonstration that it did not do so would constitute a considerable step forward as it would indicate that the road followed up till now comes to a dead end, and we must look elsewhere. In our present state of ignorance a negative answer is just as important as an affirmative one.

Entropy is the only key we have for the explanation of the evolution of the universe. It is the only notion which is not symmetrical in relation to the fourth dimension; to time. Following Eddington's apt expression, there is no other independent signpost for time in the physical world—it is the only arrow in the inorganic universe which indicates a one-way direction in the flow of time. Life, on the contrary, is rigorously irreversible in all its manifestations and asymmetric in relation to time. This irreversibility does not seem to depend solely on the increase in entropy. It seems to be a specific property of life itself. But it is clear that this assertion entails important consequences and that its scientific demonstration would be a real revolution incomparably more important than the discovery of Copernicus.

When we voice our doubts we are not always confronted by arguments based on experimental proofs but by impassioned convictions that have the irrational absolutism of religious beliefs without their consoling beauty and wealth of hope.

Now that the old determinism of Laplace has been replaced by the more supple concept of probability, we have a tendency to "think in probabilities" and to neglect the individual.

New phenomena and new properties appear as we rise in the scale of observation. Our entire human science is contained in this sentence. A single example will suffice to illustrate this statement. Let us consider a moving picture film. In its entire length, three thousand feet, for instance, it represents an action in time; the phenomenon here is the psychological drama that is represented. If, in order to study this psychological drama, we study the photographs that make up the film separately, we change the scale and we are faced with new problems. First, we pass from the kinetic state to the static state. Then, if we examine the film with a magnifying glass and afterwards through a microscope, we come upon other phenomena; the grain of the emulsion, the irregular darkening of the picture. On a still smaller scale, we come face to face with the cellulose acetate, etc. Each of these phenomena corresponds to a different scale of observation and the link which connects it to the superior scale disappears. It is clear that if we try to go over the same road in the opposite direction, namely beginning with the silver bromide to finish with the subject of the film, we cannot rediscover the directing thread which would enable us to carry out the synthesis. At every stage we separated ourselves further from the principal subject of our research, and we rapidly lost it from view.

It is the stumbling block of the analytical method. Every time we change the scale of observation we penetrate into a realm where the laws that are valid on the superior scale do not remain so *a priori*. Furthermore, in crossing the threshold which separates them and which is usually a one-way street, we may have suppressed the tenuous links, if they exist, which tied them one to the other. We may have suppressed them without being aware of it and due to the sole fact of an inadequate technique or the infirmity of the human brain. This is particulalry striking in the example I have just given, if we wish to pass from the silver bromide reduced by light on to the inferior scale; that of the electron.

We often run the same danger when, instead of going towards the tip of the funnel, we try to extrapolate on the superior scale. If we try to apply the calculus of probability to the human being, to human societies, we find that it applies on an average, as long as we stay within the limits of the very definition of probability; "The probability of an event is the ratio of the number of cases favorable to the total number of possible cases, all possible cases being considered as equally probable."

But the consequences of a same event are totally different following the indivual in whom it takes place. All Englishmen living in the reign of Charles I had an equal chance of developing a small stone in their ureter. But there was only one ureter in which a stone could have historic consequences—Cromwell's. This is not a case of a fluctuation, or at any rate there is no advantage in treating it as a fluctuation. At best it could be considered as an extremely rare combination of fluctuations. And the fact that a probability expressed by a number might be attributed to it would always be irrelevant to the facts involved.

According to the calculus of probabilities, we would be in very great danger if there were two or three million Hitlers in Germany, whereas only one would represent a danger two or three million times less. We know that, on the contrary, the danger exists only because he is unique, for if there were numerous Hitlers they would have killed each other off long ago. This last example only serves to show that the problem was badly stated and by being thus worded, it was not susceptible to being solved, for it was not homogeneous. But if the error in the above case is crude and apparent, this is not always true, and that is why these methods can only be applied in very special and always simple cases. The limitations of the calculus of probability are the same as those of any other mathematical method and are principally due to the fact pointed out above, namely the transformation into quantitative data of events that are purely qualitative. There is no difficulty whenever the answer possesses a meaning in its quantitative form. But when the meaning of the answer has to be translated into qualitative language, we come up against the impossible. For example, all goes well if we want to express the pressure inside a vessel as a function of the temperature or of the volume occupied. But if we want to foresee the properties of water from those of the atoms that constitute it; the properties of an atom from those of the protons or electrons or the reactions of an individual starting from the known characteristics of his molecules, the numerical relations are no longer of any help.

An analogous fact has been admirably and very simply expressed in the psychological realm by Emile Borel: "Common sense is no more successful than calculation in insuring against misfortune and it will always be a meagre consolation for an individual that the probability of the calamity was slight, if it is he who suffers from it."

I have neither the intention nor the time to launch into a detailed criticism of the application of the calculus of probabilities to certain problems. Moreover, Borel has done it with great perspicacity. But the fact that must be retained is that the barrier between numbers and quality seems impassable at present. Now when we say science, we say numbers.

Man may have created numbers precisely because he himself is not exclusively subjected to them. It is evident that these simple considerations lead us back to a dualism which may be only momentary but which nevertheless eliminates the slightly puerile monism that satisfied our fathers.

When we ponder over human problems, the role of the individual is of prime importance. The notion of the "average man" is entirely artificial. As Borel very justly puts it: "Social or gregarious sensitivity delights in commonplace traits. It wants all men to be similar. The Christian sensitivity, humanitarian, democratic and interdependent, would like to obliterate distinctions between egos. Amiel correctly sees in this the indication of a crude intellectuality." "If" as Pascal says, "the more one is developed, the greater differences one finds between men, we cannot say that the democratic instinct greatly develops the mind, as it makes us believe in the equality of the merits by virtue of the similarity of the pretentions." The Christian says: "Do unto others as you would have them do unto you," to which Bernard Shaw replies, not without reason: "Do not do to others what you would have them do unto you; you may not have the same tastes."

We must not think that the rigor of mathematics always exempts us from common sense. We rather enjoy making ourselves slaves to rules, thanks to which we flatter ourselves that we escape the human contingencies and the admitted weaknesses of our mental processes. But we have a tendency to forget that these rules have been created by this same brain and are consequently subject to the same causes of error. We are enamored of logic, but when we have built a system and created symbols, we lose sight of their origin and relativity and we have the same confidence in them as if they were absolute. In revenge, the very tool which has forged them inspires us with the greatest distrust. This may be a result of what is called in Freudian language "an inferiority complex." We doubt our own intelligence but have faith in methods erected by highly specialized strangers. This explanation does not satisfy me because intelligence in scientists is like common sense of which, according to Descartes, no one desires to have more than he has.

To sum up, we will say that the image we form of our universe, an image which is bound up with it, undergoes a double distortion in our brain, and we will never know the nature and importance of this distortion. The first is due to the intervention of our sensory system, which only reveals to us the qualities of the universe, that is to say, purely subjective reactions conditioned by the structure of our organs and of our brain. The second is due to the translation of the immediate information given by our consciousness, into a purely quantitative language, namely to the replacement of quality by numbers.

And finally we will say that the fragmentary, mosaic character of this image forbids us, on the one hand because of the coarseness of the weave and on the other hand because of the impossibility of viewing it in the proper perspective, to reestablish the continuity in time that our intuition alone enables us to discern.

From the scientific point of view the only thing that matters is that the coordination between the phenomena of the external world should be about equivalent to the arbitrary coordination that we have established between our numerical rules, and for a long enough time to enable us to verify the existence of an accord.

But if we refuse to admit a dualism, if we espouse the old materialistic thesis, and if, following Bertrand Russell and a few others, we only recognize chance as the unique and ultimate cause, then we must necessarily admit that we have chosen this solution by chance and that, consequently, there is one chance out of two that we have made a mistake.

SOME OF FRANCE'S GREAT INVENTORS

I have chosen only seven names amongst the great inventors who, since the end of the eighteenth century, have contributed in creating the setting of modern life. First, because a larger number would have required too much space and secondly, because I only wanted to mention those who were unquestionably precursors of our present-day world. All seven were at the origin of a human conquest or of a new industry that has developed unceasingly since their death and that nothing could foretell. As we review their lives, we will see that, from a social point of view, this rather incongruous little group symbolizes all human tragedy.

We will recognize the role of chance, good and bad fortune, dishonesty, egoism, and disinterestedness, as it exists in every realm, wherever men confront each other.

The names I will evoke are: Montgolfier, the Marquis de Jouffroy, Joseph Niepce, Beau de Rochas, Comte de Chardonnet, Louis Mouillard, and Pierre Curie.

Montgolfier invented the first airship and was the first man to rise above the earth. Jouffroy invented the first steamboat. Niepce invented photography. Beau de Rochas invented the four stroke cycle, and he was thereby the true creator of internal combustion engines (gas, alcohol, petroleum, gasoline, etc.). Chardonnet invented artificial silk from which all modern artificial fabrics derive. Mouillard invented the warping of the wings without which aviation could not have been born. And finally, Curie invented the piezoelectric quartz which constitutes a fundamental element of the radiobroadcasting stations and is used in another instrument to insure the safety of navigation.

Of these seven men, only one profited from his invention and made a fortune: Chardonnet. Two died in poverty: Niepce and Curie. Three died in abject misery. Two of these were thrown into a pauper's grave; Beau de Rochas and Mouillard. The third, the Marquis de Jouffroy died in the poorhouse.

Only one, Montgolfier, an industrialist who inherited a factory from his father, obtained a good pension and won celebrity, although his invention was not perfected for eighty years.

The conclusion is clear: invent if you cannot do otherwise, but never depend on your inventions to make a living.

We must not forget that behind these men, some of whom are famous and the others unknown, there are the pure scientists whose theoretical and experimental works made these inventions possible. They alone deserve more than one other article. But if the role of the inventor seems more modest, it requires as much genius, as much intelligence, and as many great qualities of perseverance and will, as that of the theoretician. The two complete each other and we cannot, without being unjust, give precedence to the latter over the former.

My list could have been longer but I preferred to cite only the most eminent in order to be able to devote a little more time to each one. Moreover, as we know, every great discovery has as many authors as there are civilized countries on a map. And the curious thing is that usually every country has serious arguments in favor of its thesis. Ideas are often "in the air," and without knowing it scientists or inventors come to the same solution a few days or even a few hours apart. But in the cases that I will cite, there is absolute proof that in these races the Frenchman arrived first. This, however, does not detract in any way from all those who perfected the inventions and thus made them practical and useful. They often needed as much inventive genius as the initiator, and with few exceptions the instrument or machine from which we profit today bears little resemblance to the original model. Nevertheless, there is in the contribution of the pioneer a stirring element which sheds its light upon the culture he sprang from; on the country whose son he is and which both can be rightly proud of.

Before proceeding I would like to point out the difference between a discovery and an invention.

An intellectual effort does not necessarily intervene in a discovery. It can be the result of chance and simply requires the presence of what Pasteur called "a prepared mind," i.e., a mind that can be astonished even by the most simple fact. A discovery is never looked for. One "stumbles on it." But in general, one only stumbles on a discovery when studying something else; a discovery constitutes a surprise.

For instance, Roentgen only discovered X-rays because a box of photographic plates left in a drawer were fogged by chance. Radioactivity was *discovered* by Becquerel who was experimenting on uranium. Curie *invented* the proper means to study it.

Invention, on the contrary, is the result of the intelligent efforts of a man who wants to reach a certain goal to obtain a certain result. It is a systematic effort, willed in one direction. The mental process that results in an invention is therefore a superior quality to that of a discovery.

But the difference between a discovery and an invention is often difficult to establish, for when a discovery is made by chance it becomes a goal and the spirit of invention is automatically unleashed in the brain of the searcher. From then on it functions alone, and other discoveries that are children of the hypothesis and of experimentation, often follow.

Joseph Michel Montgolfier

At Annonay, in the spring of 1783, a young man of twenty-three watched curiously as a shirt that a maid was drying over a charcoal stove billowed and seemed to want to fly away. He turned to his younger brother Jacques who was eighteen years old and said: "We will build a machine that will fly." After numerous trials, on June 5th of that same year, their machine, which was shaped like a chicken coop, finally rose above the ground carrying off with it the wisp of burning straw which filled it with hot air.

At Versailles, on September 19th, he exhibited a spheric paper balloon which rose to a height of 2000 feet under the amazed eyes of the Court and of Louis XVI. It sailed off majestically and only came down at quite a distance in the woods of Meudon. As a result of this experiment Louis XVI conferred a title of nobility on Montgolfier's father and gave him a pension of 40,000 francs.

During the month of July of that same year, the Marquis de Jouffroy had gone up the Saône in the first steamboat. But he was less fortunate than the first aeronaut and was rewarded only by disappointments.

In January, 1784—one hundred and sixty-two years ago—the Montgolfier brothers launched a huge "Montgolfiere" at Lyon. It was made of silk and paper, was more than 40 meters in diameter, and, for the first time bore aloft two passengers, J. M. de Montgolfier and Pilâtre de Rozier.

Shortly after this, the physicist Charles, tried to replace hot air by hydrogen. After that the idea fell into oblivion until the appearance of modern balloons. But J. M. de Montgolfier also invented the hydraulic ram which was later on adopted by industry.

The paternity of this invention is not contested. The first conquest of the air was truly a French conquest.

Denis Papin, 1695: *boiler*, cylinder, piston, condensation, safety valve and *turbine*.

Newcomen (English), 1711: first single-acting atmospheric engine.

J. Watt (English), 1769: patent for alternating and double-acting engine (temperature cyl. and piston).

Cugnot, 1770: *first* application to locomotion—first automobile.

Jouffroy, 1775: *first* steamboat.

In May 1768 a young squire of Franche-Comté left his province on horseback to join the Court in Paris. He was out to conquer the world, his heart full of dreams, for he had just been appointed page-in-waiting to the Dauphine.

His name was Claude-François-Dorothée d'Abbans, Marquis de Jouffroy. The place of his birth (1751) is not known with certainty, but it was either Baume-les-Dames or Roches-sur-Rognon.

He started his service when he was twenty, but was exiled to Provence after having fought a duel. There he became passionately interested in the maneuvers of oared galleys.

Back in Paris in 1775, he conceived the idea of applying steam to navigation and went to see the Périer brothers who had just built the first fire pump at Chaillot. He was twenty-four years old and it was natural that he should address himself to men who had more experience with steam than he had. The Périer brothers judged his idea impossible to realize but consented, rather ungraciously, to make a few experiments which were unsuccessful. Jouffroy, alone and without technical knowledge, persisted and succeeded in making the first steam boat—the "Doubs"—function in June 1776. It was 40 feet long and 6 feet wide.

This boat was propelled by a Newcomen single-acting engine. Its propeller was inspired by oars, or by the palmed feet of aquatic birds, but it could make no headway against the current. He then invented the paddle wheel which is still used today on the Mississippi and on many European lakes. Finally, on July 15, 1783 (163 years ago) he launched in Lyon a boat, 42 meters long and 8 meters wide, which functioned perfectly and came up the Saône to the Ile de Barbe. Members of the Academy of Lyon were present, and an official report of the experiment was made.

Jouffroy, who was thirty-two years old, then tried to float a company to exploit the "pyroscaphes" (fireboats) and applied for the needed government license. The request was submitted to the Academy of Sciences who named a committee of which the Périer brothers were members. But Périer remembered his failure in the first experiments of 1775 and voiced his doubts on the practical value of an invention that he had failed to carry out. The Academy decided that the experiment had not been conclusive.

Jouffroy not only lacked the means to continue but was spiritually crushed by the ridicule heaped on his claims that he could "reconcile fire and water." He had been nicknamed "Jouffroy the Pump."

During the Revolution he emigrated, served in the army of Condé, came back to France under the Consulate and was a witness of Fulton's first experiments in 1803. But only in 1805, and on the insistence of his friends, did he think of claiming the credit for his invention in a pamphlet entitled *Steamboats*. That same year he took out a patent... but there had already been five steamboats on the Thames for two years and that same year (1806) the first steamboat crossed the Channel from Brighton to Hâvre. In 1819, the "Savannah" crossed the Atlantic in twenty-five days.

It was too late. The country squire was not equal to the struggle. His last boat launched at Bercy on August 20, 1816, did not come up to the expectations of the shareholders. Jouffroy lived in abject poverty until 1832 and died of cholera in the poorhouse at the age of eighty-one.

His rights as first inventor were established by Arago, and Fulton himself had openly recognized them in front of the United States Courts.

Niepce

Joseph-Nicéphore Niepce was born at Chalon-sur-Saône around 1774. His father was counsellor to the king. The young Niepce served as second lieutenant in the campaigns of Sardinia and Italy. In 1794 he was appointed a member of the administration of the County of Nice. But he was obsessed by the laboratory and research. Several inventions brought him some encouragement from Carnot.

Lithography had just been invented (1812). He tried to perfect the stone and then the ink. First he replaced the stone with a pewter plate, and about 1813 he developed the ambition (considered crazy at that time) of using light in a dark room to execute the design.

After numerous trials he discovered that Jew's pitch which is naturally black, became white in contact with light and that those parts were no longer soluble in lavender oil. He therefore covered metal plates with bitumen, exposed them in the dark room, washed them in lavender oil, and spread acid over them which corroded the metal in the denuded parts. The rest of the bitumen was then taken off and he had a plate, a negative engraved in relief, from which one or several proofs could be made after inking.

He communicated his discovery in December 1827 to the Royal Society of London with plates and proofs in support of his thesis, but

164

as he refused to give the details of the process, the Society could not publish his communication.

In the meantime, a scenic painter in Paris, Louis Daguerre, who had just won a small fortune by inventing and building the first diorama, learned in January 1826, that a citizen of Chalon had succeeded in making pictures through the action of the sun. He communicated with Niepce and obtained different heliographic proofs from the trusting and naive provincial, under the pretext that as he was making similar experiments with remarkable results, he wished to compare them. But Daguerre obstinately refused to send samples of his own work in exchange. He affirmed only that he had discovered a great improvement for the dark room which provided a simpler and surer way of fixing the pictures.

Niepce suggested that they should unite their efforts and conclude a contract of partnership to give a more rapid impetus to their discoveries and make sure of the benefits. The agreement was signed at Chalon on December 14, 1829. This agreement is important, for it clearly states the relative responsibility of the two inventors:

Article I. — There will be between Mr. Niepce and Mr. Daguerre a partnership for commercial motives — The Society of Niepce-Daguerre — to cooperate in perfecting the aforementioned discovery invented by Mr. Niepce and perfected by Mr. Daguerre.

Article II. — In case of the death of one of the associates the aforementioned discovery can never be published except under the names designated in the preceding article.

Article IV. — Mr. Niepce gives and abandons his invention to the society as a working capital, representing half of the profits which it may earn and Mr. Daguerre brings a new plan for a dark room, his talents, and his activity, equivalent to the other half of the above mentioned yield.

Article XIV. — The benefits of the associates in the net earnings of the society will be distributed between Mr. Niepce in his capacity as inventor and Mr. Daguerre for his improvements.

To be fair, it must be recognized that as soon as he was initiated into the methods of Niepce, Daguerre contributed an immense improvement which amazed Niepce himself. He replaced the pure bitumen with a bitumen solution in the lavender oil and exposed the plate to petroleum vapors.

Alas, Niepce died four years later and Daguerre imposed a new contract on his son which states: "I, the undersigned, declare by the present writing that Mr. Louis-Jacques-Mande-Daguerre, painter and member of the Legion of Honor, has made known to me a process of which he is the inventor. This new process has the advantage of reproducing objects 10 or 10 times more quickly than the process invented by my father, Mr. Joseph Niepce. Following this communication made to me, Mr. Daguerre consents to abandon to the society the new process of which he is the inventor on condition that this new process should be known under the sole name of Daguerre..."

And later it became daguerreotype.

Daguerre received a pension of 6,000 francs and the Niepce family a pension of 4,000 francs.

Niepce died poor. Daguerre, who was above all a business man, nevertheless gave proof of a real talent for invention, but, as says the *Larousse* —"reservations must be made about his integrity."

Curiously enough, it was a cousin of Niepce, Claude Niepce de Saint-Victor who finally invented photography on glass (June 12, 1848), which supplanted the process on paper invented in England by Talbot and which was presented to the Royal Society long after the original work of Niepce and Daguerre.

Around 1880 a young twenty-year old polytechnician was on vacation at his home in Besançon. One day he amused himself by watching a spider, who was letting itself down by one of its threads. After following it first with his eyes and then through a magnifying glass, he thought there was no reason why we should not be able to do the same thing. It was the starting point of one of the most important industries in the world: artificial silk.

Hilaire-Louis-Marie, Count Bernigand de Chardonnet, graduate of the Department of Civil Engineers, tendered his resignation, married Mademoiselle de Ruolz (niece of the inventor of the silver that bears his name) and patiently and methodically pursued his dream.

He started from gun cotton (cotton plus nitric acid) which when dissolved in a mixture of alcohol and ether produces collodion. We will not speak of the difficulties encountered in obtaining a completely homogeneous gun powder (pyroxylin) which is completely soluble in ether-alcohol. As none of the commercial nitrocellulose were perfect, Chardonnet made a thorough study of pyroxile (C. R. Ac. Se. 1888) and found a way to manufacture it in quantity without endangering the workmen (nitrous vapors).

He then invented a kind of glass nozzle with a very fine orifice and a machine that could spin uninterruptedly under water.

By using hydrated nitrocellulose he succeeded in spinning in the open air. With collodions filtered on a layer of coton wool, he finally succeeded in spinning unbroken threads 40 kilometers long which weighed one gram for 1500 meters (3 kg. 300 to cross the Atlantic).

An arrangement of pumps and regulators invented by him obtained a uniform thickness. The threads, rolled around spools, were twisted on a winch (his first patent) which gave its name to the new silk; winch silk. This solid thread was first sold as a sewing silk. Soon he made materials which after 1895 were known by the name of "Chardonnet Silk."

He worked entirely alone and took out forty patents. This was the origin of *all* artificial tissues and of all chemical fibers from rayon to nylon.

Beau de Rochas

In the outskirts of Paris, near Vincennes, there lived around 1880 a queer individual, a kind of tramp who existed almost entirely on public charity. Saint-Mande and Vincennes were still villages at that period and market gardeners, hawkers, and flower girls with pushcarts were the only inhabitants of the suburbs of Paris. The individual in question was not a market gardener. He had no possessions. Nobody could buy what he had to sell, and he himself could buy nothing — not even a pair of shoes; not even a hat. He could be seen strolling towards Paris, wrapped in a large cape, shod in canvas shoes or sandals, and bareheaded. There was no jacket under his cape, not even in winter, but when they saw him pass, the good people of the village exclaimed, "What a shame! A man like that who is educated — a scientist!" And proud of having a scientist in their midst, the people—whom he did not always know—provided him with food.

It was true. Beau de Rochas, the tramp, was a scientist. He was even a man of genius. He had been an engineer of the Compagnie du Midi. Then when he was about thirty, he became the prey of a fixed idea and tendered his resignation. In 1862, he had taken out a patent which had interested no one except a few members of the Academy of Sciences. It was for an invention which was apparently of purely theoretical interest. Later, the Academy even gave him a prize. Five years before his

171

death the Society of Encouragement for National Industry gave him another one. But prizes do not go far towards paying for a room, a little food from time to time, and buying paper and pencils.

What he had invented was very simple: the gas engine, the petrol engine, the Diesel engine, or more exactly the fundamental principle at the base of *all* these engines; *the four-stroke cycle.*

Only the Lenoir motor of 1860 existed at the time. It was a very imperfect gas engine and so inefficient that it was hardly used. Two years after Beau de Rochas obtained his patent, Otto in Germany took out another patent, entirely based on the one by Beau de Rochas, and built a gas engine in 1836 which utilized the Beau de Rochas principle. This economical engine was the starting point of all so-called internal combustion engines and created a revolution. *It was the engine of Beau de Rochas.* Otto made a fortune. For many people the Rochas principle became the Otto principle or cycle.

In Vincennes, Beau de Rochas continued to walk in his big cape and his sandals with his hair blowing in the wind. And then one day in 1892, exhausted, discouraged and ill; he died. There was no money. And so it was a pauper's burial with one horse and an old unpainted hearse. But strange to say behind the usually unaccompanied and pathetic carriage a crowd dressed in black followed gravely. It was the *zone*— the small market gardeners, the little vegetable and flower hawkers, and all the poor people of the villages of Vincennes and of Saint-Mande— who accompanied "their scientist" to his last resting place. They had fed him for years, simply because he was hungry and because he symbolized science, one of the things most respected by the French people, who are Cartesian without knowing it. Never had so many flowers been seen on such a shabby coffin; that day the little flower girls did not take out their pushcarts to sell their flowers.

There was also one well dressed man, decorated and all alone. He was the great chemist, Sainte-Claire-Deville who represented the Academy of

Science. But the heart of Paris had shown more perspicacity than its brain; more greatness also.

Eighty years have passed since this admirable invention. Nothing has been changed; the cycle of Beau de Rochas is still the standard cycle of all modern engines. It was not perfected because it was perfect from the start.

This has since been realized; a little late! Beau de Rochas now has a monument at the Conservatory of Arts and Crafts in Paris. It is more durable but less moving than the spontaneous homage of the *zone* to its tramp of genius.

Louis Mouillard

In 1856 a twenty-two-year-old man, son of a traveling salesman of Lyon, *was the first to travel a distance of about thirty meters through the air*, upheld by wings made of wood and silk. How many Frenchmen know his name? It is a very modest, very plebeian name: Louis Mouillard—a great name.

On September 20, 1897, a poor devil who lived entirely on charity, died at the age of sixty-three, in a modest room of the Mousky in Cairo. It was Louis Mouillard. He had started his first experiments at the age of fifteen and since then had been in turn, a drawing teacher, a guide for tourists, a bookkeeper, a public scribe, a herbalist, and a haberdasher. He had become infirm, but a devoted woman who was almost as miserable as he, took care of him. She was beside him when he died; gently, without noise, as befits a derelict.

In the quarter where he had lived for thirty years, everyone knew him, from the Franciscan Father to the Arab or Nubian watercarrier; he was called the mad Frenchman—*Magnoun el francawi*. How else could he be characterized? He had established his laboratory on a terrace between laundry lines hung with washing. A chair, a table, a telescope and a box of food scraps for the birds. As soon as he appears they flock around him. In a neighbouring courtyard, with the complicity of the Sisters of the Good Pastor, the precursor of aviation installed his birds, his traps, his poor instruments, and his machines.

This madman, constantly immersed in his dream, dragging his misery and his faith; this madman who is laughed at when he runs down the slopes of the hill with canvas attached to his shoulders; whose book *The Empire of Air* published in 1881 is impossible to find; this madman borrowed all his inspiration from the birds. As almost all geniuses who are forerunners, he knew he was right, but he came much too soon. By way of a testament he wrote this moving phrase: "And this is aviation; I give it to the world." The sub-title of his book reads: "Essay on ornithology applied to Aviation." As epigraph, only one word: "Dare."

In his childhood, on the borders of the Saône, two little friends occasionally pay him a visit. They are the sons of Daudet, a dealer in silk scarves and are called Ernest and Alphonse.

At the age of fifteen, Louis Mouillard, with the help of his sister had already built a pair of wings. They were made of ticking and were held up by the whale bones of a corset. But not until he was able to buy an eagle, did his real life begin.

A persevering study of the bird convinced him that the great mathematician, Lalande, was wrong in affirming that a surface of 127 square meters was necessary to hold up a man. Although Louis Mouillard enrolled in the Paris Beaux-Arts School and worked in the studio of Ingres, he did not cease observing birds on the towers of Notre-Dame or in the Jardin des Plantes. After his father died, Louis goes to Africa to breed stock on a farm of the Mustapha. But his main occupation is still birds. Along the sea shore, the stormy petrel, the wonderful long-winged bird of the tempests, gives him the idea which will henceforth direct all his experiments. He writes: "The bird tells me to remember that in aerial steering the basic question is speed. I have understood this well. Speed, always speed, produced by a fall, by a current of air, produced if one wishes by the beating of wings. It is always the power that sustains and without which air does not uphold."

Prophetic words of genius.

He was evidently ruined in a short time. He then accepts the post of drawing master at the Polytechnic School of Abbasich, near Cairo, and renews his study of the flight of birds. The falcon, the vulture—but above all, the kite. The drawings he has left are striking. He describes them all; the pelican, the swallow, the wagtail, the sparrow, the dove, the hoopee, the blackbird, and the heron. Finally he affirms that: "The flight of the vulture can be reproduced with a single, rigid surface, on condition of possessing the two directions—vertical and horizontal." He writes his last book: *Flight Without the beating of Wings*. Alas, he is stricken with hemiplegia and dies in 1897.

His inheritance refused by the family, was sold at public auction for 32 francs.

But before his death he had been in correspondence with the American engineer, Chanute, to whom he unveiled the results of his experiments and in particular the secret which allowed the Wright brothers to really fly, namely the warping of the wings that he discovered in the vulture. In one of his letters addressed to Chanute, (November 20, 1890) he writes: "I have ideas which in more active hands than mine would be quickly executed and made productive, beginning with aviation which through you, I give to the world."

In reply Chanute sent 2,000 dollars to the inventor as a payment on account for the utilization of the common patent.

175

Chanute did not start his experiments until six years later, when two small bicycle manufacturers, Wilbur and Orville Wright, ordered their first plane. He then applied the governing ideas of Mouillard—the vertical rudder and the warping of the wings which, for the first time, enabled them to stay in the air. The Patent Office of the U.S. government joins the names of Mouillard and Chanute. The Wright brothers loyally recognized what they owed to the French madman. In an interview cited by Henry Coüannier, they said: "We were on the point of abandoning our work when the book of Mouillard fell into our hands, and we continued with the results that you know."

None of the other inventors had seen the light—Tatin who made a few models in 1879 and even Ader who spent nearly two millions in experimenting on gliders from 1890 to 1897 abandoned his trials although his plane, with batlike wings, succeeded in making a leap of about 100 meters. *None of them* had had any presentiment of the fundamental secret—the warping of wings. Langkey, in America, had only failures; Lilienthal, in Germany, killed himself in 1892. Only the line Mouillard-Chanute-Wright triumphed, thanks to the genius of the first named and the intelligence and admirable tenacity of the others. In 1903, the first glider, controlled by warping, rose into the air. On October 6, 1908, Wilbur Wright flew for four minutes. On December 18, he covered 100 kilometers at a height of 110 meters in one hour and fifty-four minutes.

The Egyptian section of the French Aviation line organized a subscription fund to raise a monument to Mouillard. The monument bears this inscription:

He discovered flight without the beating of wings and invented their warping and the combination of warping with the rudder.

"The bald statement does not tell all," writes one of his chroniclers, Edouard Herriot. "It does not say how much will, love, disinterestedness, observation, and analysis, were needed to arrive at this result which has so deeply transformed the life of men. It does not tell the tragic destiny of this great scientist, this great poet, thrown one day into a pauper's grave. The madman of the sky was buried in the earth without a sign. Thus it was for Molière. Thus it was for Mozart."

Pierre Curie

No school, no university. For teachers—his father, who was a doctor, and his brother Jacques. Love of natural science. Curiosity about nature. He starts mathematics at the age of fourteen and proves to be brilliant. He is a good swimmer and a poet. He likes the arts, painting and music, is absent-minded, slow, and a dreamer. The following quotation is taken from the diary he wrote when he was twenty and describes him better than I possibly could: "Weak as I am, everything around me would have to be motionless to enable me to keep my head from being turned by every puff of wind, from yielding to the slightest pull. Or were I hurled like a humming top, the friction itself could render me insensible to external things. When I try to launch myself by rotating slowly, the slightest thing—a word, a story, a paper, a visit—can stop me and postpone or delay forever the moment when, endowed with enough velocity, I could concentrate within in spite of all my surroundings. We must eat, drink, sleep, idle, love, taste of the sweetest things in life and yet not succumb. When doing all this, the unnatural thoughts to which we have dedicated ourselves must remain dominant and continue their impassive course in our poor heads; we must make a dream of life and life of a dream."

From the very beginning he was preoccupied with the notion of symmetry. "Everything is a question of symmetry." he said, around 1880. Pasteur came to the same conclusion independently.

The symmetry of crystals interested him passionately. With his brother Jacques, he studied the crystals of Rochelle salt, tourmaline, and quartz. He published with Jacques but wrote his fundamental report on the *Principle of Symmetry* alone.

Finally the two brothers discover piezoelectricity, a consequence of the principle discovered through Pierre Curie's intuitive genius.

Incidentally, *all* the experiments on radioactivity from 1890 to his death, were made thanks to the piezoelectric quartz and to the instruments (ionization chamber and electrometer) invented by him. He was assisted in his work by an excellent technician, Madame Curie, and by Debierne and J. Danne.

Today, *all* transmitting posts use the piezo quartz and *all* boats have ultrasonic sounding machines based on the use of the piezoquartz.

Curie's discovery of radioactivity and the study he made of this new phenomenon, although it made his name famous, are not more important than his theoretical work on symmetry. I will not speak of it here as I am limiting myself to inventors. It is the invention of the piezoelectric quartz, so important in itself, that qualifies Curie as a great inventor.

Let us now throw a glance backward.

Montgolfier is ennobled, receives a pension of 40,000 francs. He is an honored industrialist, a celebrated inventor. He is happy. And yet his effort was a hundred times less deserving than that of Mouillard, who died alone, in poverty, without friends, without a name, and who was buried in a pauper's grave.

Jouffroy d'Abbans, a country squire, suffered approximately the same fate. Niepce dies poor and his children do not even have the decency to defend his name against a greedy, unscrupulous collaborator. Beau de Rochas is thrown into a pauper's grave like Mouillard. Chardonnet makes a fortune, and the great Curie disappears in the shadow of his wife—precious and able collaborator without doubt, but whose ability was only a reflection of her husbands genius which died with him.

I could have mentioned many others: Jacquard, inventor of the loom; Moissan, inventor of the electric oven which Héroult was the first to apply to the manufacture of aluminum; the Lumière brothers; Dagron who invented the *V-letters*, microphotographed and transported by carrierpigeon during the war of 1870; Thimonnier, who in 1830 invented and built the first sewing machine *which really functioned* (*Webster* attests the fact); Marinoni, who invented the rotary press, thus making it possible to print great quantities at a time—and many others.

I could have mentioned even those men who have been exalted by the daily press following a small invention of purely momentary importance and who lived a long sterile but honored existence without ever doing anything else, like Branly. Such good fortune is rare.

In any case, chance only favored those who arrived at a time when minds were prepared and ripe. To succeed, genius alone is not sufficient. One must be born at the right moment. It is as dangerous to come too soon as too late. Or else we must, like Montgolfier, make a spectacular invention which *appears* to be perfect immediately.

The great innovators, the true geniuses, are those who discover not so much machines as the principles which will never age and will direct human activities for one or several centuries, like Denis Papin, Carnot, Mouillard, Beau de Rochas, and Pierre Curie, to mention only the discoveries which have molded world industry. We must expect to see many decades pass before curious minds ask themselves the name of the initiator who most deserves the gratitude of the world.

Without any displaced national vanity, we can say that in this domain, France occupies a place of honor.

To end, let us try to judge the production of the great inventors, no longer from the practical point of view of the advantages we derive from their works, nor from the economic or intellectual point of view, but from the purely human one—the point of view of civilization.

In the broadest sense of the word, civilization can be considered as the manifestation of the tendency which pushes man to dominate his environment and to dominate himself. In this guise, civilization represents an effort in view of an ever—increasing freedom from hunger, from cold, from fear, from illness, and from pain, which have menaced man for millenniums. Liberation from all enslavements, the enslavement of distance, of time—vanquished by aviation and radio—and finally, the enslavement bequeathed by our animal ancestors: the enslavement of the appetites, the passions, and all the carnal memories inherited from the beast. Although we have progressed magnificently in the material realm, it must be admitted that we have not achieved much progress in the moral, spiritual realm.

The combination of these two efforts, on the one hand, the material effort towards the liberation of the body, and the moral effort towards the liberation of the spirit which follows it, therefore represents the contribution of man to civilization. But, as I tried to show in a book recently published, civilization is nothing but the form taken by evolution from the day of the appearance of man on earth.

The scientist, the inventor are therefore the artisans of one part of this evolution; the philosopher and the priests are the artisans of the other. They are not always aware of it, but their roads tend towards the same ideal although often masked by specialization and ignorance. They will unite one day, but humanity is still too young to enable us to predict when this result will be attained.

What I wanted to show is that in this soaring of all humanity towards a goal, indistinct for some, clear for others, France has played a role of prime importance—an inspiring role. She has always been at the vanguard of progress; in the philosophical realm with Descartes, Pascal, Lamennais, and Bergson, as well as in the scientific realm with Cuvier, Lavoisier, Lamarck, Laplace, Ampère, Pasteur, Claude Bernard, Curie, Louis de Broglie, and a hundred others.

We have just seen that the same is true in the industrial realm. Let us not reproach France for not having always known how to extract from her genius what others extracted for her. Her role is to keep alive a flame which illuminates the way like a beacon but is not made to heat a boiler. Like a thoroughbred she will jump obstacles and win races, but she cannot be asked to pull a plough. Where there is nothing she will create something, but when that something has emerged from nothingness, she often loses interest and goes off in search of another desert to fertilize, for that is what she loves.

Alas, this dazzling unconcern has cost her dearly. Fifteen hundred thousand men in 1914-1918; three hundred thousand in 1940. How many since then? And how many others, having lost all reason to live, will only be living corpses in their homes devastated by barbarians?

But let there be no misunderstanding. France has poured out her light on the Western world for centuries. She has behind her a tradition with roots so deep that no cataclysms of human origin can destroy them. The ideas which she distributed welled up from her very substance as naturally as war has overflowed from Germany for the last two thousand years. From all these tragedies, France emerged, sometimes transformed in her aspect, but at heart truc to herself and always alive. Just as the bee secretes honey and wax, France secretes art and thought, and, no matter how poor and unhappy she is, the secret of beauty, taste, and clear reasoning must always be sought at her side.

Her scientific, industrial, artistic, literary, philosophical, and moral credits will never be paid. Certainly she has made grievous mistakes for which she has paid with her blood and her martyrdom—her material destruction. But beneath the ruins, the light did not go out. It is only eclipsed. France has played an incomparable and slightly nonchalant role in evolution. She will once again take up her mission of inspiration when her wounds are healed and will continue, because she cannot do otherwise, to fulfill her duty which is to enlighten.

THE ROAD TO REASON

The importance of the subject that I intend to discuss in this chapter can be easily understood by casting a mere glance at our civilization and actual society. We need not be great scholars to realize that they are both very sick. Without pretending to diagnose the ailment, which is infinitely complex, we can I think state, without fear of making a mistake, that the difference between the development of knowledge and that of the moral qualities of man is one of the fundamental causes of the world crisis.

Roughly, this difference manifests itself in the following manner: human knowledge, the conquest by man of the physical world (science in its broadest sense) has advanced with giant strides during the last century. When he considers only this aspect of what he calls progress, man is overcome by pride. The ancient myth of Genesis, the myth of the science of good and evil, which shows man succumbing to his curiosity, to his thirst for knowledge and losing by that very fact the peace of heart and soul which characterizes ignorance, has only gained strength. It already summarized the experience and wisdom of numerous generations thousands of years ago when science barely existed. This alone would suffice to prove that man has not changed, that his reactions have not varied when confronting nature, and that the responsible elite was already worried about his future for the same reasons as today.

Ever since he has lived in society, man has remained so much the same that we are confounded when reading the sacred Hindu, Chinese, or Hebrew books which contain the rules recognized as necessary by the sages. "The final goal of life is not knowledge but action," said Huxley. This view is perhaps rather terse, but it is true that the progress of knowledge should be encouraged to the extent that it can serve action, or the moral elevation of man, and not as a mere means of acquiring knowledge. If this is not understood in time, humanity may be overwhelmed by the events which already begin to escape its control, and it is possible that man in the near future will be unable to profit from the tremendous advantages that science has put at his disposal.

Can science contribute to the development of the moral qualities? Is it legitimate to think that these two realms can influence each other? Moralists and philosophers of all ages have raised this question. In his admirable book *Man the Unknown* Dr. Carrel also considered the problem and showed that under certain conditions far from being realized in our time a positive answer might be given. This is the optimistic point of view. On the other hand, is it not true that moral qualities like art, and unlike science and industry, seem unable to advance beyond a certain degree of perfection which always remains the prerogative of a very small number of individuals? Today when we want to qualify a noble action, do we not say that it has an antique majesty or beauty?

History teaches us that great events have always been directed by the spiritual potential of the people. It is the isolated individuals endowed with exceptional spirituality who have oriented human evolution. Can science from now on play the role which was assigned to them? When looked at from a higher point of view the history of humanity is nothing but the struggle between the noble impulses, the spirit of sacrifice, of devotion, of renunciation, the cult of a spiritual ideal, the detachment from material pleasures, and the low impulses which, on the contrary, are based on the search for purely physical enjoyment. History also teaches us that numerous civilizations which attained a high degree of perfection preceded ours, and that they all disintegrated the moment their goal seemed to be attained, when life became so easy and agreeable that the responsible leaders were submerged by indolence, deprived of their virtues, and transformed into brilliant puppets, either cowardly or cruel. Conscious of this moral decay the people, by means within their reach, then prepared the advent of new leaders endowed with all the qualities the others had lost. One can almost say that extreme comfort coincides with the decline of a civilization or at least foreshadows it. The public baths of Caracalla and Diocletian, even though built for the people, were more luxurious than anything we can imagine but sounded the deathknell of the power of Rome.

We have to recognize that though science is the fruit of our curiosity, and as such praiseworthy in itself, scientific results have always been used to further material progress and not moral progress. It can be argued that this material progress is the result of applied science and not the goal of pure science which only seeks truth. But what is this truth?

Is curiosity really the highest incentive of our nature as Renan believes? This is doubtful, for curiosity was certainly not the driving force that inspired the great prophets of humanity: Buddha, Confucius, Moses, and others. Neither curiosity nor science inspired St. Vincent de Paul or Joan of Arc. Hence there exist in man, but alas not in all of us, other aspirations than the sole love of life and the simple thirst to know the biblical myth. And it so happens that the influence exerted by these men whose activity sprang from more noble desires has been felt through the centuries and is still alive today in spite of the tangible successes of pure materialism to which we owe the wonderful development of what we call modern civilization: the conquest of pain by anaesthetics, the prophylaxy of contagious diseases, sterile surgery, radio, cinema, automobiles, planes, and also—to be fair—the long range cannon, the machine gun, and mustard gas.

According to Renan, science enables us to seek the truth. Furthermore, it brings us the only possibility we have of improving our material fate; this is the aim of applied science—namely of the art of the engineer and the doctor. Finally, it preserves us from error, says Renan, who adds, "It is already something not to be duped. The man who is trained by its

185

disciplines—those of science—is definitely more admirable than the instinctive man belonging to the age of faith. He is exempt from errors into which the uneducated person is inevitably led. He is more enlightened, he is less sublime and less absurd. One can say that this is no compensation for the Paradise that science takes away. Who knows if science takes it away? After all no one is impoverished when worthless bonds and counterfeit money are taken out of his pocketbook. A little good science is better than much bad science. We err less when confessing our ignorance than when we imagine we know many things we do not know."

These lines are taken from the preface to *The Future of Science*. It is easy to detect the uneasiness of an honest man who feels the urge to convince himself and to absolve himself at a ripe age, for having made a choice based on motives that appear rather frail as a prop for the lever of reason when they are deprived of the support given them by the passion of youth. But Renan falls into the error common to all theoreticians, writers, and philosophers. He thinks he speaks of Man when in reality he is speaking of Renan, and he forgets that humanity produces very few Renans.

We will study successively these fruits of science, the search for truth, the elimination of error, and the improvement of human conditions. The two first represent the ambitions of pure science. The third, the application of the discoveries to the welfare of humanity.

First of all what do we mean by truth? It is clear that there is no absolute truth, and that this expression is devoid of meaning. It can only be a so-called "scientific truth." How can we define it and from what does it derive its prestige?

The definition of scientific truth given by Buffon still seems valid: "A frequent repetition and an uninterrupted succession of the same events is the essence of physical truth." However, frequent repetition is not always necessary. Condillac is more abstract in his description : "All truths are restricted to the relations between simple ideas, between complex ideas and between a simple idea and a complex idea."

In mathematics an obvious identity is often considered a truth. Every one remembers the criterion of truth which constitutes the first principle of the method of Descartes. The relative character of scientific truth is therefore unquestionable.

The aim of science is not so much to search for truth, or even truths, as to classify our knowledge and to establish relations between observable phenomena in order to be able to predict the future in a certain measure and to explain the sequence of phenomena in relation to ourselves. These relations are called laws, and when no exceptions are known they become scientific principles. Laws or principles always rest on measurements, that is to say relations: relation of the quantity measured to an arbitrary quantity taken as a unit.

Astronomical laws, for example, enable us to foresee the movements of the heavenly bodies with great precision: eclipses and the periodic appearance of certain comets are thus calculated several centuries in advance. Physical laws, also expressed in the stenographic language called mathematics, enable the quantitative prevision of what will happen when such and such conditions are fulfilled: the pressure of a mass of air of a given volume at a given pressure will be doubled when it is compressed so as to occupy only half of its original volume. The product: pressure multiplied by volume remains constant by a first approximation: $PV = P'V'$. This is called Mariotte's law. We can understand the mechanism of this phenomenon by means of ingenious hypotheses, such as the kinetic theory of gases. Chemical laws enable us to analyze and synthesize very complex bodies. Recently it has been possible to obtain by synthesis substances normally secreted by the endocrine glands : hormones (thyroxine for instance) and vitamins.

Does this mean that these laws have an absolute existence outside of the presence of man? No. On the contrary, they only exist because of his presence and do not possess any significance outside of him. Indeed what is the difference between a scientific law and a social law which we endeavor to respect? The difference lies in the fact that man must obey the social law and that if he fails in this duty he commits a major or a minor crime. On the contrary, if it is demonstrated that a phenomenon does not obey a certain scientific law which was considered established up till then, it is the law that is wrong and must be modified as quickly as possible so that it will apply to the new facts without ceasing to apply to all the preceding facts. The word "obey" has a very different meaning in the two cases. It is always a rule promulgated by the human brain. But the social law is an arbitrary rule established *a priori* and possesses an absolute authority based on the interest of the community and perhaps also on a kind of innate idea which is very difficult to define but is nevertheless powerful; namely, justice. Whereas in the case of the scientific law we only have the trial of a relative rule established *a posteriori* with the sole aim of describing the succession of a group of correlative phenomena.

But what do we mean by "phenomena"? A superficial analysis of this concept soon shows that it is based on observations and that these observations are only possible through the intermediary of our senses. For example, when we speak of the fall of a stone, a phenomenon which characterizes what we call gravitation, we mean to speak primarily of the succession of sensorial perceptions which have accompanied the real objective phenomenon inside of us. We have seen the stone on the table. We have seen the gesture which pushed it toward the rim, we have followed the fall, the displacement in space, we have heard the noise resulting from the brutal contact with the floor. All this is entirely subjective. Science takes this succession of sensations, of physiological reactions, disengages the abstract ideas and enables us, thanks to our generalizing intelligence, to deduce therefrom universal concepts such as time, space, and gravitation. Symbols assigned to these concepts confer upon them a kind of individual existence which enables them to enter into our formulae, but this existence is entirely relative to us and is a result of the confrontation of man and the phenomena. Our law of the fall of bodies therefore simply aims to give us a means to foresee the place that any object, abandoned to itself in a free fall, will occupy in relation to our system of reference at a given moment of this fall and its speed at the end of so many seconds. In other words to foresee the place where we can observe it, see it; i.e., once again, a subjective sensation.

Therefore, the general value of the laws of nature only has significance if we refer ourselves to a certain type of perceptive faculty, that of the normal human being. It possesses no significance outside of man. In relation to the universe, man plays to a certain extent the role of the radiophonic receiver which registers the electromagnetic perturbations, the Hertz waves, and transforms them into a melody. Without the receiver we are surrounded by silent vibrations of different wavelengths but do not perceive their existence. If there is no eye to intercept a ray of light there is only obscurity. In the first analysis, the clearest benefits we have derived from pure science consists therefore in a fairly complete knowledge of the relations between certain mechanisms that are external to us and our reactions to these mechanisms. In the second analysis, we perceive that we are totally ignorant of the very nature of these mechanisms inasmuch as we can only imagine them by basing ourselves on subjective physiological reactions. And in the third analysis, we observe that all the phenomena that we are capable of observing are statistical phenomena, and only represent, on our scale, the resultant of an immense number of elementary phenomena at an imperceptible scale.

The following example will enable us to understand more clearly the real nature of the information given by science. Let us take a cylinder with a piston and a manometer, a pneumatic pump in other words. Normally this pump is full of air or of some kind of gas at the surrounding pressure. Let us make reference marks on the body of the pump: the first corresponding to the maximum volume (the whole cylinder), the second to half of that volume, the third to a quarter, etc.

The rough idea derived from the experiment is that, naturally, if we force the piston to occupy the second position, that is if we oblige the gas to occupy half of its original volume, the pressure will be increased. Mariotte's law expresses this result quantitatively by saying that the pressure will be doubled. But the explanation of this phenomenon does not follow, although we are so accustomed to these facts that they appear evident. The scientist is endowed with a curiosity that is less easily satisfied.

To explain these facts Mariotte had to resort to the following hypothesis, which is still valid. The gas is constituted of an immense number of minute molecules, which, as we know by other experiments, are endowed with extremely rapid movements in all directions. Each molecule—with a diameter of about one ten-millionth of a millimeter—comports itself like a true missile with its trajectory only limited by the shocks against other molecules and against the walls of the pump. It travels between two shocks about one tenth of a thousandth of a millimeter in a straight line and is subjected on an average (at the ordinary temperature and pressure) to 5 billion shocks per second. It is the statistic resultant of these shocks against the walls which determine the pressure of the gas. This hypothesis is called the kinetic theory of gases. The explanation of Mariotte's law follows immediately: if we bring the piston to the second guide mark, the number of shocks per second will be doubled (the volume being reduced by half) and the pressure due to the kinetic energy of the molecules will also be doubled. Therefore, compression simply acts by increasing the number of shocks of the molecules in the cylinder and the piston.

Pressure, on our scale, is therefore no longer a simple phenomenon but the consequence of an immense number of elementary phenomena. Mariotte's law is a statistical law *as in general are all our scientific laws.*

Its precision is the result of the great number of molecules in presence. The fact that the walls of the cylinder receive two or three million shocks more or less is of no importance, the molecules are so light that the difference is much too small to be measured by our most sensitive instruments. The increase of the sensitivity and precision of the measuring methods therefore tends to enable them to register the actions of a smaller and smaller number of molecules. But we are incapable of studying and foreseeing the path of an isolated molecule; we cannot seize the individual, drowned in the mass. The greater the number of molecules the greater the precision obtained. As there are about 30 billion molecules in a cubic centimeter of air, the degree of precision on our scale is high.

We now perceive the nature of the scientific answers and the nature of the precision obtained. This precision is high only if the number of elementary particles is high, but its increase in no way increases our knowledge of the subjacent phenomena. It is clear that the precision would be very low if, instead of millions of millions of molecules there were only ten. In the latter case a single impact, either more or less, would bring about an error of ten percent. We know that in living organisms, on the cellular scale, there exist anatomical elements that are so minute they can contain only a small number of big molecules; hence the "fluctuations" which perhaps play an important role in the characters of species in evolution. These fluctuations still exist. The more they digress from the average the rarer they are; they escape calculation, do not obey our statistical laws, and have been the object of deep study.

It is evident that our laws are only approximate global laws, valid for us on our scale of observation, but incapable of giving us any information on all the laws of the constitutive elements that are revealed by analysis. Our laws are only verified on condition that the movement of the elementary particles is absolutely disordered. The marvel is that it is from this compulsory disorder that the order of the universe, the persistence of the species, and the brain of man are born.

The nature of our universe is discontinuous and granular: it is formed of molecules. Nevertheless, we derive an impression of continuity that only the closest analysis enables us to destroy. Electricity is also discontinuous: its ultimate elements are the electrons. Whenever analysis is pushed far enough, we do not observe the continuous anywhere in nature. And yet the continuous is the foundation of our representation of nature in all its domains. Is this solely the effect of our human brain? The problem is beyond us but is clearly set.

We know how printing plates, or more exactly halftone engravings, are made. When examined through a magnifying glass they reveal a texture which is more or less coarse according to the paper on which it is printed; this texture divides the picture into small squares of equal size. These small squares when taken individually cannot possibly reveal their role in the entire picture. They are black or gray, but that is all one can say. If we examine the picture at a normal distance without a magnifying glass we can recognize the portrait or subject represented, thanks to the apparent continuity, only due to the distance of the eye. The discontinuity in space melts into a very definite continuity in our eye. A film, composed of a series of motionless subjects, none of which can alone reconstitute the entire episode, acquires the power to evoke continuity in time, movement, and life only as a result of its rapid passage in the machine : 24 frames per second.

Science has enabled us to analyze the phenomena of nature in a great number of cases and to reach the elements which, like the example of the plate, contribute to the creation of the phenomenon. This is certainly an important result, but it is about all that we have obtained. We have never yet understood the concatenation, the evolution, and the harmony perceived by our intelligence on a superior scale but which escape analysis.

Renan was unaware of all these facts that were discovered later. He thought that science would diffuse light and dispel the darkness because it had explained eclipses, thunder, and a few other phenomena that had terrorized humanity in times past. "A little good science is better than much bad science," he said. But he did not foresee that *much good science* would reopen many questions and would propound still greater problems inasmuch as we cannot at present conceive that they can ever be solved by the human brain.

The thorough study of the elementary constituents of the atoms, electrons, protons, and neutrons, has led man to doubt determinism, which was the corner stone of the rationalistic theories and which only exists on our scale or on scales that are superior to ours. Determinism, also is statistical. The works of Heisenberg have introduced a "principle of indeterminacy" into science which revives the humility that we had made the mistake of forgetting. The works of Louis de Broglie and Schrödinger forbid any attempt to represent mechanically the elementary particles which only derive their reality and their qualities from their movement and which can only be conceived scientifically in the form of a group of equations. In brief, the universe would be ultimately constituted of time and space. As far as we are concerned, its reality would be the consequence of the conjunction of these two concepts which, from our human point of view, have no significance when they are considered separately.

And living (biological) time is not the time of the inert things which surround us.

That is the point we have reached. Does this mean that we have attained truth? But what truth? We still do not know how an egg produces a bird or a reptile. We have simply succeeded in establishing formulae expressing ratios; formulae which enable us to foresee our own reactions to a certain degree and in cases which are often arbitrarily simplified. To revive Plato's old image —when certain shadows appear at the back of a cave we sometimes know the ones that will follow. But we are not and cannot be in communication with the objects which project these shadows except by means of the shadows themselves. We sometimes even know the expedients that will determine the appearance of certain shadows. But we are not very far advanced if we have to explain the nature of these Chinese shadows by groups of equations.

Let there be no mistake; pure science is admirable and the results obtained are passionately interesting. Our only reason for showing the fragility of its answers is to caution the layman against the scientific mystic which cannot withstand an honest examination but which has been used as a tool, or rather a weapon, against the spiritual mystic. The prestige of scientific superstition, in accordance with the tradition of all superstitions, rests on a carefully nurtured ignorance of the crowd, but it must not prevent the free man from thinking freely.

We have attempted to show that the answers given by pure science to the questions asked by man are on the one hand conditioned by the structure of our sensory organs and of our brain. This was evident *a priori*, but on the other hand we are led to admit that phenomena can only be explained by means of statistical laws and that these laws cannot take into account individual elementary phenomena but only the resultant of an immense number. This absolute limitation gives an essentially relative value to scientific "truths" and prevents us from understanding the evolution and order of the universe.

We also spoke of the fluctuations that can occur and modify the normal development of phenomena in an unforeseeable manner.

We come across the same facts no matter on what scale of observation we place ourselves: the subatomic scale, the scale of human beings, or the scale of human societies. We always perceive the existence of great amorphous masses which obey certain more or less precise laws and the existence of individual fluctuations which escape these laws.

Like a stream following its course, humanity slowly progresses toward unknown ends. But a stream sometimes encounters irregular ground on its way and is forced to fall from a great height. We know that man can no more oppose the current that sweeps him along than a drop of water can return to its source. The immense majority of molecules which make up the mass of water are not separated from it, but the foaming waterfall enables a certain number of them to escape; they form a veil, a light mist which floats in the air and no longer obeys the laws governing the shape and the direction of the river. A sunbeam pierces the clouds and this gray vapor is illuminated by a rainbow. The iridescent cloud has sprung from the cascade, but it is not the waterfall which is ablaze; it is the droplets which escaped from it.

Likewise, the artistic and intellectual capital of a country or of a race, is only due to a small number of individuals who have risen above the crowd and whose personality instead of simply reflecting the light breaks up and refracts it into its colored elements. The waterfall, the whole river, glory in the rainbow; yet the question has often arisen whether it is not the ponderous mass of the stream that should be given primary consideration since it is this mass that traces its path towards the sea and operates the factories.

Now if we try to characterize a people or a nation, we perceive that only a very small number of men symbolize the whole mass. Since the tenth century only three or four hundred Frenchmen have represented France, its civilization, its culture, and the French spirit. They are the rainbow. The role of some hundred million "average Frenchmen" has been to create it. Up till now this creation has been entirely due to chance. It is the fluctuations that have caused the statistical laws to be upset. In a word, great men are monstrosities, but monstrosities on which civilization depends.

We can ask ourselves whether the aim of science should be to increase the number of exceptional beings or the happiness of each individual. Individual happiness is difficult to define and is often in contradiction with the common good.

What are the means for bettering the condition of humanity given us by science? We need only look around us to discover a thousand. We go out into the street; if we are not run over we can find rapid and comfortable means of transportation; if we are run over we are taken to beautiful hospitals where we are operated on painlessly. These hospitals also take care of the people who have contracted illnesses due to urban agglomerations. With a little luck, life as a whole has become easier and less precarious. Everything tends to suppress effort, to standardize ambitions, tastes, and distractions. The average man, the typical citizen, instead of trying to satisfy his true aspirations, those that are a consequence of his physiological and moral self, is involved, in spite of himself, in occupations and pleasures which are imposed on him, without his being aware of it, by the simple fact that he lives in society; the press, cinema, and radio, reveal examples of existence to which he is not adapted but which tempt him. If he has not succeeded in modeling his life on these examples, he feels persecuted and his existence is a perpetual cause of complaint. He completely loses sight of the true joys that are within his reach and cannot conceive life without the material advantages that his neighbors, or even the inhabitants of faraway countries, enjoy. Jealousy and envy make their appearance, and he ends by desiring things not for themselves, or because he really wants them, but because his neighbor has them. And when he acquires them himself he often has a momentary satisfaction of vanity and not a real durable joy. The science of mechanics does not only produce beautiful automatic machines. It distorts humanity.

Every invention is marvelous in itself. Its consequences are often tragic. Not only its physical consequences (accidents of all kinds) but its moral consequences. Men caught in the toils only seek their joys in material pleasures and only want to escape themselves. How many radios function all day? Every available moment must at all cost be filled by noise or pictures. Ambitions are increasingly limited to mediocre enjoyments represented in films as the ideal to attain. And thus for the great majority of men, life—real life—goes by without touching them and without their even being aware of it.

In brief, the problem from a practical point of view is the following one: the benefits of science, applied without discernment at the will of captains of industry whose business it is to make money, or of governments led astray by primitive philosophies, do not take into consideration the nature of man or his real interests. That is why science, which is at the base of all that we call our progress, incurs a grave responsibility.

A manufacturer of dynamite would be severely judged if out of pure generosity he distributed his wares to grown up people and to children. Dynamite is necessary in our civilization: our roads, our ports, our tunnels, our mines consume great quantities. But its distribution is carefully regulated, thanks to which there are few accidents. I believe science is equally dangerous. Taine wrote that "science is not healthy for everyone." The ancients, beginning with the Egyptians, had already realized it. Their science was modest compared to ours but remained the prerogative of a small group of men. This state of things was not ideal because people's intellectual value is rarely on a par with their moral

value. But the principle can be defended, and in any case the danger was limited. Nowadays this is no longer possible.

Nevertheless, it seems evident that no scientific discovery should be considered without its accompanying social consequences. It does not behoove me to decide on whose shoulders this grave responsibility should fall.

Let me make myself clear: the foregoing applies not only to inventions and applied science but to pure science and scientific theories or hypotheses. Any of these could be found at the source of all actual social movements. Renan said: "Our true reason for defending primary education is that a people without instruction is fanatical, and a fanatical race always creates a danger for science as governments are in the habit of imposing intolerable constraints on freedom of mind." There is a strange innocence in these lines! Did he really imagine that primary education suffices to kill fanaticism in man? It is fanaticism itself which is dangerous and not the idea which serves as its pretext. It is a pity that he did not live long enough to contemplate the dreadful excesses of anti-religious fanaticism.

It is alas impossible to suppress fanaticism or to give all men the wide culture necessary for impartial judgment. This is a utopia for there are certainly not ten men in a hundred who are physiologically adapted to assimilate it.

What then is the solution? I will not presume to suggest one, but I will quote a few more lines from that great writer, that great honest man, and great infidel, according to the Church, whose liberty of thought is unquestionable and whom I have already quoted several times: Ernest Renan.

The following lines are taken from the preface of his famous book *The Future of Science*. In reviewing his manuscript after a year's absence, he judges it himself in the following words:

A warm current relaxed my severity; almost all my illusions of 1848 crumbled and appeared impossible. I saw the fatal necessities of human society; I resigned myself to a state of creation in which a great deal of evil conditions a little good, in which an imperceptible quantity of aroma is extracted from an enormous *caput mortuum* of wasted material. I reconciled myself in several respects with reality and when on my return I reviewed the book I had written a year before, I found it bitter, dogmatic, sectarian, and harsh...

"The idea of a civilization based on equality, as evoked by certain pages of this work, is, then, a dream. A school in which the pupils would make the laws would be a sorry school. Light, morality and art will always be represented in humanity by a magistracy, by a minority, guarding the tradition of truth, goodness and beauty. But in order to maintain its power, this magistracy should not have recourse to impostures and superstitions nor be allowed to dispose of force.

"There were also many illusions in the accord I gave, in those ancient days, to the socialistic ideas of 1848. Though I still believe that science alone can ameliorate the sad condition of man here below, I no longer believe the solution of the problem to be as near as I thought it then. Inequality is written in Nature; it is the consequence of liberty, and individual liberty is a necessary postulate of human progress. This progress implies great sacrifice of individual happiness. The actual state of humanity, for example, requires the maintenance of nations which are very heavy establishments to carry. A state that would give individuals the greatest possible happiness would probably be a state of profound degradation from the point of view of the noble pursuits of humanity.

"... Between the two objectives of political concepts, greatness of nations or well-being of individuals, we choose through interest or through passion. We have no indication of the will of nature or of the goal of the Universe. For us, the idealists, only one single doctrine is true: the transcendant doctrine according to which the purpose of humanity is the development of a superior conscience, or, as was said formerly, the greatest glory of God. But this doctrine could not serve as a practical political goal. Such an objective must, on the contrary, be carefully dissimulated. Men would revolt if they knew they were thus exploited.

"... To sum up: though the incessant work of the 19th century has greatly increased the knowledge of facts, the destiny of mankind has become more obscure than ever. The grave problem of the future is that we do not see how humanity can be given in the future a sufficiently satisfactory catechism without a return to credulity. It is therefore possible that the downfall of idealistic beliefs is destined to follow the downfall of supernatural beliefs, and that a real abasement of morals dates from the day on which humanity saw the reality of things. It had been possible to obtain, by means of myths, a surprisingly high moral effort from the kindhearted gorilla; take away the myths and a part of the simulated energy that they awakened will disappear."

200

The preceding lines are clearly not the ones that are quoted when one speaks of *The Future of Science*.

But let us ponder the last sentence for an instant: "It had been possible to obtain, by means of myths, a surprisingly high moral effort from the kindhearted gorilla; take away the myths and a part of the simulated energy that they awakened will disappear." The kindhearted gorilla is humanity as a whole, the stream I mentioned above. I will not insist on the word "gorilla" which depicts the attitude of Renan towards the majority of human beings and which illustrates the conflict, not to say the inconsistency, of the philosophers' opinions on the subject of the necessity of a primary education. I will come back to this later. But if some one said to us today: "From now on we have found the way to enable the 'kindhearted gorilla' to live without any struggle on his part," there would be no more social problems. In return, we must not count, henceforth, on any moral, intellectual, or spiritual effort, for these efforts were due to a simulated energy developed by myths that we have replaced by precise rules. No other joys but material satisfactions: eat, sleep, pro-create. No more art, no more beauty, no more enthusiasm, no more sacrifice, no more illusions. Seventy years of existence guaranteed without accidents or anything unforeseen. Seventy years of the existence of a mollusk. This is the solution of all social problems. If we were told this would we not have the right to answer: give us back these myths which differentiated man from the animals? The life of the ant hill or of the termite's nest is not suited to living beings who can pride themselves on noble lives, magnificent gestures, generous impulses, disinterested acts of courage, moral grandeur, or artistic and intellectual masterpieces which are proof that after all something has taken place between the Neanderthal and modern man. The majority do not appreciate these joys? Perhaps, but I am not sure. But who can say that what man should be proudest of is not precisely the fact that he has given birth from time to time to beings who live on a higher plane than that of the termites? Who can say that this is not precisely his role in the universe? Science teaches us that though our general laws are statistical laws in which the individual particle plays no part, it is probable that the particles which escape the statistical laws are the ones which determine and orient the evolution which we observe but do not understand.

We have demonstrated that the complete impossibility of foreseeing the future was a consequence of a certain fundamental principle of our science. It is just as logical to help certain individuals to rise above themselves and above the crowd as it is absurd to try to transform every individual into a scholar. Renan tells us that equality exists nowhere. Is this an indication that we must seek to increase the existing inequality? Does not the fundamental difference that separates man from the animal lie precisely in the fact that he can increase this inequality? When we want to train champions for foot races, the high jump, or boxing, we do not give the same care to all those who have already been selected from a great number. What is done for a sprinter should be done for a man destined to shine in the intellectual or moral realm, and it is our duty to use all the means that are capable of developing in him the genius which differentiates him from the others and of which we will be proud one day, even if the most efficacious means consist in these myths. Moreover, how can we explain that these myths are the only food transformed by man into moral values, into beauty? Is not this a proof of their reality? The word reality may seem inappropriate in this connection but what is left today of that reality on which yesterday's science aimed to build its temple? We know that for science all reality consists of groups of equations without material support: we only know absolute space and absolute time which have no separate existence and which are concepts born in our brain. Myth for myth, is it not probable that the truest ones are those which obtain results from the kindhearted gorilla that the others are unable to attain? When in the laboratory we are beset by doubts on the cause of a phenomenon, when we hesitate between two possible material causes, we accept as the efficient cause the one which is followed by the phenomenon. The phenomenon which interests us in man is what differentiates him from the animal, namely on the one hand his creative power, his abstractive power, and his artistic power and, on the other hand his moral value symbolized by his idealism, his tendency to "develop a superior conscience," and his respect of principles which imposed themselves on him: the notion of good and evil, of justice, of duty. The origin of these qualities escapes us. But if we do not know what determines the first, we all know what brings about the others.

Science, or rather a few pseudoscientific philosophers, thought that a clean sweep could be made with impunity of everything that was not forces and molecules. They thought these were realities and facts. We have learned that molecules and atoms only acquire their reality with respect to ourselves through velocities and accelerations. These are purely abstract concepts like forces. This is the foundation of our materialism. Who would dare affirm today that this alone enables us to attain the joy of life and the formation of this superior conscience of which Renan speaks. Let us listen to him again for he will answer us and let us measure at the same time his intelligence, honesty, and illusions: "I say frankly: I cannot imagine how the foundations of a noble and happy life will be rebuilt without the ancient dreams. The hypothesis in which the true sage is the one who neglects wider horizons and confines his outlook to vulgar pleasures is absolutely repugnant to us. But it is not the first time that the happiness and nobility of man appear unstable. Let us then continue to enjoy the supreme gift that has been bestowed on us : that of existing and of contemplating reality."

Alas, in all of humanity which consists of about two billion human beings of all colors, how many men are capable of following this advice and of being content with it? Could the sage of Treguier believe in all conscience that the kindhearted gorilla would content himself with the enjoyment drawn from contemplating reality? It is hardly likely, but a conflict had arisen in the soul of Renan who though an aristocrat in the Grecian sense was terrified by an aristocracy in the social sense which he knew rested on religious foundations. He did not dare face this conflict. He may not even have admitted it to himself.

Let us now glance back and examine the road we have traveled together. Though it is impossible to arrest what we call material progress, which by itself apparently cannot assure the happiness of the individual, the satisfaction of all his aspirations, and the development of his moral being—though it may be impossible to go against the stream —it is to be hoped that the moral education of children, of all children, will retain the attention of nations as much, indeed even more than their intellectual education. Nobody would think of making a fine embroidery on fragile or coarse material. The only way in which we can progress is to prepare a firm canvas worthy of the embroidery that will enrich it; i.e., build up generations endowed with strong physical and moral health. It may be that Renan was right, and that the only way to prepare these morally strong and noble generations is to have recourse to the myths that he admits we cannot do without. I defer to the authority and intelligence of the philosopher. His opinion, which was daring for his time, has acquired considerable weight in the light of modern science, for we now know what scientific truth consists of and that the ultimate nature of our universe 'escapes our intelligence. If a similar ideal could be attained one day; if humanity could become strong enough to conceive science as the crowning of the edifice and not as its foundation; if scientific workers considered their work as a mission and not as a springboard, then we could have hope, for science can still do much to improve our condition, to decrease our suffering, and to exalt our spirit.

Man has had the choice between two roads to happiness. The one is smooth and satisfies that thirst for knowledge, that curiosity to which we owe our science. It is an easy, agreeable road favorable to all appetites and rich in benefits of all kinds. The other is hard, painful, thankless, and without tangible profits; it requires a rigorous discipline, unceasing self-denial and treats the body as an enemy. The only reality recognized by the first road is the material world. The second, on the contrary, admits as an important reality only imponderable spiritual forces. The first road seemed to be the most logical one, and rightly so, as long as we could believe in the existence of a simple material reality; of a solid basis to our universe. It is natural that a certain elite should have chosen it. Analytical sense and pure intelligence found ample sustenance in the harvest of experimental facts that were lacking in the second one.

But when it was realized—it was not really so long ago—that the ponderable was formed of the imponderable, that analysis was limited by the very structure of our brain, and that beyond the order and harmony of the world man only discovered disorder and chaos, then the question arose whether, after all, the second road did not correspond to a reality as deep as that which our unaided intelligence can conceive; *or if truth did not lie in a combination of the two roads*. I will try to make myself clear.

All the activities of a human being are strictly interdependent. They are, on the one hand, the consequences under various aspects of his physiological reactions. But on the other hand, his physiological activity depends in part on his nervous system and on his affective life; his emotions. Every man at a given period of his life may be characterized in very different ways: from an anatomical point of view, from a physiological, pathological, chemical, and physicochemical point of view; from an esthetic, intellectual, moral, social, and even sentimental point of view. Any portrait that takes into account only one of these sides is accurate but incomplete. And yet we often judge the people around us on fragmentary pictures of this kind. But all these portraits, like photographs of a monument taken from every possible angle, are the resultant of one single complex phenomenon: *that* man.

The reactions of that man in the intellectual as well as on the moral or purely physical plane are only the echo of the biological, physical, and chemical reactions of which his body is, or has been the seat. The whole constitutes a definite unit. It is impossible to separate any of these activities arbitrarily without impairing the unity of the individual, for nobody yet knows exactly how these various functions influence each other. But we already know that a cretin is generally a being whose thyroid gland functions badly, and that sexual inversions are a conse-

205

quence of other endocrine disorders. The emotions react directly on the economy of the body and bring about chemical reactions through the intermediary of the nervous system. If, then, we consider man from this point of view, it is clear that neither of these two tendencies that confront each other—on the one hand absolute materialism and on the other absolute spiritualism—represents an intelligent, human point of view. Neither the one nor the other contains a practical solution to the social problem, for they each take into consideration only half of the human being; not man as a whole. As I said before, it is through a combination of the two points of view, and with a less intolerant more scientific attitude, that the sociologist and the statesman must in the future consider the problem.

Many philosophers and scholars have realized, in all ages, that the true incentives of humanity are psychological and non-material. Bergson wrote somewhere: "I have sometimes asked myself what would have happened if modern science, instead of starting from mathematics to orient itself in the direction of mechanics, astronomy, physics and chemistry, had begun by studying the spirit, if Kepler, Galileo, Newton, for example, had been psychologists."

Clearly many purely physical incentives exist. But they may only be a medium to enable the spiritual forces to manifest themselves. Hunger, often love and fear, have a physiological basis; we must live. But only so as to obey the mysterious command: the species must persist. On the other hand, who can pretend that it was love of life or the necessity to procreate which sustained and inspired the Spanish cadets in the smoking ruins of the Alcazar?

Country, flag, respect of the given word, any ideal—all that makes the dignity of man and his honor—are they not all waging a perpetual struggle in opposition to the physical self with its appetites and even its most natural aspirations? The emotion we feel in the presence of a fine act, a magnificent work, or an emblem that we venerate is a reality that we can be proud of as men. It is a reality that raises us above the animals, just as does intelligence. If the suppression of this reality in us were the goal of science, then I would say: "woe to humanity, woe to science!"

But this is not the case. It is only the goal of a small number of scientists whose minds are too narrow to take in the complexity of the world and to understand its beauty. They refuse to admit that man is not nourished by bread alone. Yet the most rabid revolutionaries know it so well that they destroy a mystique only to replace it by their own and tear down a flag only to hoist another in its place.

The role of science can and must be great on condition that its limitations are not lost sight of, and that we remember the words of Renan, meant for other disciplines, but which the philosophical schools of the nineteenth century have endowed with a broader general character. They can be summed up as follows: light, morality, and art will always be represented in humanity by a minority which keeps the tradition of truth, good, and beauty. But this minority must not be given power nor allowed to maintain its authority by impostures and superstitions.

The sole attitude of man towards science should be that of Pasteur, who in 1875 said at a meeting of the Academy of Sciences: "Science should never trouble itself about the philosophical consequences of its findings. If by developing my experiments I could demonstrate that matter can organize itself into a living cell or a living being, I would proclaim it in this precinct with the legitimate pride of an inventor who is conscious of having made a discovery of capital importance, and if I were provoked, I would add: so much the worse for those whose doctrines or systems are not in accord with the truths of natural facts. It is with the same pride that I told you a short while ago, while defying my adversaries to contradict me, that in the actual state of science the doctrine of spontaneous generation is a myth. And I add with the same independence: so much the worse for those whose philosophical or political ideas are thwarted by my studies."

And as I have evoked the immense figure of Pasteur, let me end by quoting from his last speech, given at the Sorbonne during the ceremony in honor of his seventieth birthday. They are amongst the most beautiful and moving lines that were ever written.

"Young men, young men, entrust yourselves to the sure and powerful methods of which we only know the first secrets. And let all of you, no matter what your careers, keep yourselves from sterile and belittling skepticism; do not let yourselves be discouraged by the sadness of certain hours that pass over a nation. Live in the serene eace of the laboratories and libraries. First say to yourselves: 'What have I done or my instruction?' Then as you progress: 'What have I done for my country?' until he moment when you will perhaps have the supreme joy of thinking that you have contributed something towards the progress and the good of humanity. But no matter whether our offorts are more or less favored by life, we must, when approaching the great goal, have the right to say : 'I have done what I could.'

THE FUTURE OF SPIRIT 1941

The moral crisis which has prevailed since the beginning of the century rests on two misunderstandings, the first of which can be said to date from the beginning of science and therefore goes back about two hundred years. I will try to explain it briefly. Up till now, two tendencies have opposed each other: the intellectual tendency and the moral and religious tendency. As long as the intellectual tendency could not rest on the homogeneous and logical whole that we call science, it could not fight against the religious tendency which had been deeply rooted in man for thousands of years—ever since the most ancient prehistoric times. But as soon as man learned to look at his universe and have doubts about the accord of certain dogmas with the observed facts, he attempted to shed some light on the hitherto mysterious phenomena that surrounded him and endeavored to reduce the supernatural realm and increase the intellectual realm. Whenever he honestly attempted, without any preconceived idea, to soar into the scientific realm, he was brought back to earth by outmoded traditions and moral and physical sanctions. As the only thing with which he could reproach himself was a passionate interest in nature, and as his sole ambition was to reveal truths to the world, he considered these sanctions unjust. This was the first misunderstanding. The priests, who were accountable for the maintenance of morality and the spiritual future of man, were responsible for this error which is best illustrated by the condemnation of Galileo.

If at that time they committed an error of judgment, they were only partly to blame, for their entire intellectual formation tended to separate them from pure intelligence and reduce them to the role of defenders of tradition. They could not know that the most important rule of the universe is evolution and that if eternal truths, transcending human intelligence, exist they can in no case be shaken by new facts as these facts are perforce of divine origin. They mistrusted intelligence in which they saw the hand of Satan, the Prince of intellectuals, and did not understand that well-directed intelligence is less dangerous than stupidity. It represents the only tool which enables us to conceive the greatness of immortal creation. They were afraid of it, and instead of associating themselves with it in order to guide it, they tried to fight it. This was an error for they thus alienated those who should never have left the Church; they made enemies of the scientists. Intelligence is divine, but the way it is used is not always good. The priests of bygone days lacked faith in nature and replaced it with faith in traditions which may have had a divine origin but which had become humanized and often deformed in the course of centuries. They believed in a static world when everything around them revealed a marvelous dynamism. They asked for miracles when, as Henri Poincaré said, "The eternal wonder is that miracles do not occur all the time." If this were not the case, the universe would be ruled by whim instead of being subject to laws which derive from their harmony and coordination a power and a beauty that are immeasurably higher.

The Church therefore deprived itself at that time of the very people it most needed. She condemned them and thought she personified both God and religion, thus sinning through pride. She set herself up as an absolute tribunal and accepted as allies the lowest category of her followers in order to crush what she thought was a menace and which was, in reality, a natural evolution. It is the attitude of the Church which is partly responsible for the "allergy to priests" from which France has suffered.

The intellectuals were in turn responsible for the second misunderstanding which started with the Encyclopedists and, from the doctrinal point of view, the birth of positivism. But it had already existed potentially for many years before that. Its extreme form consists in the belief of scientists and philosophers that the conflict between science and religion is insoluble because "the hypothesis God" is unnecessary and science alone can explain everything. Morality being a necessity and not of supernatural origin, they created secular moralities and enthusiastically adopted absurd doctrines which were more or less copied from religious doctrines. They could not understand, any more than the monkey of the fable, why humanity was not entranced by their magic lantern.

For fear of being unjust towards materialists who were sincere but lacked light, we will refrain from bitterly criticizing the modern defenders of secular morality. We will merely point out that they are simply victims of a scientific inaccuracy—the last vestige of errors which were formerly professed but are now rejected. The sincere materialists and positivists are, alas, also ignorant. They still rely on the physics, chemistry, and biology of 1880. But there have been important upheavals in those realms since then, and we can state without exaggeration that the proud intellectual edifice which at that time represented the picture of the universe has crumbled and only the stones remain. These stones are the scientific facts which when they have been well observed are indestructible. But we have already known for over twelve years that the edifice which is being built at present with the help of the same materials will not in any way resemble the former one.

We cannot ask people of a certain age to go back to school. Their brains have lost the plasticity of youth. I am afraid that the materialist, the honest layman, is no longer capable of giving the intellectual effort needed to understand how oldfashioned he is. We must simply hope that the younger generation, who have inherited from their parents certain traditions now outgrown and completely incompatible with the actual progress of science, will one day have enough curiosity or wisdom to learn and admit that they were lied to.

The moral crisis, which is not ended, rests, as we said, on these two misunderstandings; on the one hand, the failure to recognize the value of science and on the other hand, the overestimation of its value has caused the separation of these two aspects of human activity. As a result, moral progress has lagged behind intellectual progress, and it is from this lag that we are suffering. The progress of science cannot be checked. The prestige of the Church—and as a consequence that of the moral doctrines she was supposed to diffuse and uphold—has been weakened by the prestige of a new star; science.

Attacked by reason, or by the scientific reasoning that takes its place, the Church employed anathema for her defense. She would have been wiser to employ the same weapons as the adversary and to demonstrate his weakness. Faith cannot be given through the intermediary of reason, but it can be demonstrated that reason has never been able to give a serious argument against faith. This demonstration can be rigorously scientific and that is what I attempted to do in my book *The Road to Reason*.

Jules Lachelier, a great French philosopher, wrote the following remarkable sentence: "I am afraid that there is something empirical in the French mind and that the only way to make it admit a truth is to present this truth as an experimental fact." The French character is completely analyzed in these few lines. It is this "five-and-dime" Cartesian philosophy which has brought us to where we are. We can criticize it, but we must take it into account. By failing to do so we commit the same error as the Church which in the past misunderstood the evolutive, dynamic character of the human spirit, underestimated the role of intelligence and science, and did not take into consideration the revolution introduced into the world by printing.

The error of rationalism lies in the pride and incomprehension of man. The positivists reasoned like irresponsible children. They did not see that man, when deprived of an absolute rule of conduct, resembles a climbing plant without any support. The questions which trouble him remain unanswered. He no longer even dares to ask for an explanation, or else in his distress he consults those who though unqualified inspire

214

confidence by their moral qualities or their professional honesty. These, in turn, vainly interrogate themselves and all, or nearly all, advance in life filled with anguish, like children lost in a forest at night who instinctively stretch out their hands in the hope of finding other helpful hands. Vain and unconscious men, under pretence that the light which guided them in the past was unreal, have raised opaque veils covered with obscure symbols in order to hide the light. Adepts of an absolute determinism and causalism, they have seriously infringed upon their own laws by rejecting without proof the existence of a cause, the effects of which could not be contested. Like the little schoolmaster, drunk with his knowledge, and because they deemed themselves able to forego everything that was not rational, they decreed that all humanity should also go without.

But the formulae, the equations which satisfy them, have no meaning for the masses. A mathematical mysticism will never touch the heart of the people any more than the chemical analysis of a painting can evoke the esthetic impression it produces. Hypnotized by a summary materialism, they thought they possessed truth, but this word has only the meaning we decide to give it. There are only relative truths whenever the sensory system intervenes. Yet the materialists admit the reality of the electron, also only observed by its effects and which is essentially a creation of our brain. It is an indispensable creation, but a very disturbing one, since the works of Louis de Broglie, Schrödinger, and Heisenberg. Time, space, matter—all have a meaning on our scale of observation, but they lose it completely as soon as we reach the realm of subatomic corpuscles. Nothing links the properties of the molecules to the properties of the atoms. The reality of things? For the physicist it is at present nothing more than groups of equations which become more complicated every day. As to the problem of life, it remains for us what it was for Pasteur.

Must we then abandon all hope of building a bridge between science, produced by the human brain, and the highest aspirations of the human soul? Must we admit that the rational cannot be reconciled with the irrational, and that the role of intelligence is limited to throwing confusion into the hearts of men? Personally, I cannot believe it.

I am convinced that the religion of the future will lean on science, for there can be no discord between the observation of nature and human truth. Truth can only exist in harmony; reason and intelligence must demonstrate this harmony. This demonstration will rally men of every opinion and suppress an artificial conflict, based on ignorance, which tends to maintain an ambiguity which is incompatible with human dignity and the majesty of divine creation. Moreover, this conflict only rests on the human interpretations of the sequence of facts and these interpretations are relative and momentary. A correct interpretation always exists, and it is the only one. This interpretation cannot be challenged and represents the aim pursued by science which often hesitates and gropes, as does nature itself. Science is very young when compared to the moral, spiritual, and religious ideas of humanity. It enjoys the prestige of a new toy. But we must not be misled. In spite of its youth and imperfections, it constitutes the best means of convincing us of the immensity and harmonious beauty of the universe, revealed by the infinite complexity of the apparently most simple phenomena. It is an orderly and confounding complexity which is a thousand times better qualified than ignorance to make us feel the omnipotence of the Creator.

If, as Lachelier said, it is true that the only way to make the French mind admit a truth is to present this truth as an experimental fact, then the duty of the scientist of today is to make every effort to correct the errors of the old interpretations and to attempt to propose new ones capable of demonstrating the unity of the universe; a unity that only the ignorance or bad faith of our predecessors could have called in question.

I will try, briefly, to expound such an attempt. It is the result of long years of meditation, and a part of its interest may derive from the fact that, having been brought up in the indifference of the end of the nineteenth century and without any religious faith, I have been compelled to admit the necessity of the idea of God and religion by the same scientific facts which supposedly had the opposite effect on the rationalists. It is therefore on the territory of science that I combat them and in agreement with the most illustrious scientists of the past and the present: Newton, Pascal, Lavoisier, Faraday, Maxwell, Ampère, Raleigh, Pasteur and, amongst the modern Nobel prize winners, Millikan, Compton, and many others in the United States. If I offend certain convictions, I ask the reader to excuse me and consider my attempt as an effort to conciliate two tendencies in the human spirit. Their opposition has had disastrous effects and it must disappear.

A difficulty arises, or seems to arise, from the beginning. As I said we are on scientific grounds. But there is a fact that the Church only accepts with regret or not at all, i.e., the fact of evolution. The argument invoked has no great scientific value for it rests on the Holy Scriptures, the Bible of the Hebrews. Without wishing to flatly contradict this attitude, it can nevertheless be said that though the first book of Genesis may be of divine inspiration, it was certainly written by human beings. Just as it is now admitted that the "days" of the creation in reality represent periods, we must admit that the other terms must not be given a literal, usual meaning. I will not even mention the glaring blunders which are found in profusion in the Scriptures as a result of faulty translations. The value of this admirable myth is to be found in its symbolism and disappears if it is considered as stemming from experience.

I do not know any theologians, but I do not doubt that the orthodox attitude towards evolution has already evolved of itself. Moreover, we will see that even when taken literally there are two facts in the first two chapters of Genesis which to my knowledge have not been explained satisfactorily up till now. They can be interpreted in such a way that the conflict which was supposed to exist between the Holy Scriptures and evolution no longer exists.

Though we are inevitably led to accept evolution, this does not mean that we know its mechanisms. Evolution imposes itself on us because we perceive a progressive complication in the structure of organic beings. This complication attains its apogee in the human being and in his brain. But an immense number of problems remain to be solved.

To cite only a few, I will remind the reader that the cells of the most elementary animals and plants, infusoria, paramecia, and amboeae, are fully as complex as those of superior organisms. As I have said before, the very origin of life remains absolutely mysterious and no attempt to manufacture living matter has ever succeeded. The evolution of species, which represents just a small chapter in general evolution, is the only one in which a satisfactory lineage has been established. The hypotheses of Lamarck, Darwin, and de Vries, when combined, enable us to understand in a certain measure—especially for the mammals—the successive passages from one form to another. An interesting sequence, for example, has been established in the Equidae (ancestors of the horse) starting with the Eohippus of the Eocene period (forty or fifty million years ago) about as high as a hare with four toes on his forefeet, up to the horse of our day with a single toe. The progressive recession of the toes can be followed through five intermediary forms where they are at first external and finally hidden under the skin, as in the last of the series, the modern horse. This sequence does not explain the mechanisms of the passage from one to the other.

But it is less easy to establish the origin of the Eohippus and to follow his ascending line, and as soon as we try to discover the origin of the large groups—the orders, the classes, the phyla—we are practically disarmed. We must admit that in most cases, they seem to have appeared suddenly. How could it be otherwise when all these findings are based on fossil bones, often incomplete and buried for hundreds of millions of years?

To draw a lesson from evolution, we must stand back in time and span a period of about two thousand million years. The study of radioactive deposits shows that the earth was created around that period, give or take a hundred million years. This was the beginning of the first stage of evolution. Life—an inconceivable, unbelievable phenomenon—appeared a thousand million years later when the earth crust had cooled sufficiently. There is at present only one possible hypothesis to explain this phenomenon: creation of a supernatural origin. This hypothesis is not scientific, but there is no other. A second stage of evolution starts from then on and is apparently governed by new laws. The laws of matter continue to be valid for inorganic elements, but the great fundamental principle of Carnot-Clausius which reigned supreme in the inorganic universe seemingly ceases to apply rigorously to living organisms. Finally, a million years later, the third stage begins: the evolution of man, the evolution of spirit. The Carnot principle ceases to apply. Evolution as a whole can therefore be considered as a series of efforts tending towards a progressive liberation from the great laws of inorganic matter and, in particular, from the second principle of thermodynamics.

Now we must face the facts. There has been an evolution, and this evolution has been ascendant. Man is more complex and more perfect than the other mammals, the mammals than the birds, the birds than the reptiles, the reptiles than the fish, and the vertebrate fish than the mollusks. Everything therefore takes place as if it had been decided from the very start that evolution would lead to man.

I must make my meaning clear. When I speak of man I do not mean the human form but human personality, the psychological characters that differentiate man from the animals; not the fact that he walks erect and uses his hands, nor that he has articulate speech.

This is the point that differentiates the final hypothesis we propose from all those advocated up to the present. It may be useful to point out that no theory of evolution escapes the necessity of introducing a finalism. Certain authors have admitted it frankly; Lamarck for instance. Others, like Darwin, have only spoken of the role of the Creator without giving any details; others have not mentioned Him, as De Vries, who dealt only with a mechanism limited to the characters of the species. Still others, like Weismann, who developed and generalized the works of Mendel, admitted a first cause and believed that man with all his morphological characters was "potentially" preformed in the initial cell, the original amoeba, more than a thousand million years ago. He admitted, furthermore, that all intermediary animal forms were thus preformed.

I hasten to add that his theory is no longer taken seriously by anyone.

The finalism which I invoke is very different. It is a telefinalism that acts as an orienting force, somewhat like gravity acting on matter, or the North Pole on a magnetic needle. Let me define my idea by an illustration. If a large mass of water is progressively released from the top of a mountain, it will flow in a thousand different directions in numerous streams of various configurations which will follow a dissimilar course according to the obstacles they meet on the way. No stream will exactly resemble another; some will flow in an almost direct line; others will follow varied trajectories, more or less slow or rapid, circumventing different obstacles or forming small lakes. Some will mingle with others and grow larger. Others, on the contrary, will dwindle and finally disappear into the soil.

But all of them, drawn by the acceleration of gravity, will always descend toward the bottom of the valley, even if only one succeeds in reaching it. It is thus that I conceive the directing effort of evolution. The ultimate goal to attain is the spirit, the human soul, consciousness. The intermediary stages were no more individually foreseen than were the trajectories of the different streams.

The normal play of the laws of nature (chance) functioned from the start, but the efforts were *directed*. There were an immense number of trials: only those which showed a real progress were maintained and continued to evolve. The failures sometimes persisted—a great number still exist today—but they were on the fringe of real evolution which through all these different forms followed its course ineluctably, until the moment when a being finally emerged that was capable of harboring, protecting, and perfecting the masterpiece of creation, the human mind, the support and tool of consciousness.

We will see later on why this material support had to be as perfect as possible so as to shelter a brain capable of giving birth to consciousness. The inconceivable complexity of the human brain is revealed to us by our sensory organs and by its own subjective functions; thought and consciousness. This complexity is therefore revealed to us through

itself. The objective picture we form in our brain is only one of the consequences of its structure. The brain conceives itself. This is unimaginable, but true. It is very probable that if an organ of that type was created at the end of a thousand million years of trials, it was meant to accomplish certain functions and not simply to exist as such without any functional activity. It was not a question of beating a record of complexity, or of manufacturing an incomparable museum piece like the concentric, sculptured ivory balls carved by several generations of Japanese. Thought and consciousness were therefore meant to exist one day. Spirit was then *willed*; the brain was only its support, just as the human body is the support of the brain.

Only one other possible hypothesis exists: namely that man, his brain, his spirit are entirely due to chance. The book we mentioned above, *The Road to Reason*, is consecrated to demonstrating the fact that everything had taken place in the history of the earth and of life as though chance had been perpetually directed by an anti-chance. It is simpler to call this anti-chance—God.

If the spirit has been willed, it must be the crowning result of evolution. Consequently, the sole object of all evolution— with its still mysterious bifurcations, its monstrous creations, its imperfect trials, its marvels, and its cruelties— was to assure the advent of the final superior goal: not man but SPIRIT.

Evolution continues, but the brain exists. We have ascertained the immense superiority it confers upon the human being, and have convinced ourselves that no purely anatomical or physiological advantage would be capable of assuring a greater supremacy or more unlimited future possibilities. We therefore do not conceive that this evolution can continue in the anatomical realm as it has done up till now. We cannot conceive that we could develop an eye in the back of our head, or a supplementary hand, or wings. On the contrary, we can well conceive that the future development will take place on the spiritual, moral, and intellectual plane and that the ultimate end will be a superior conscience and a spirit delivered from the material burden, from the ancestral chains. Much has to be accomplished in that line. For in the mass, the brain, the organ of thought, is subject to the body more than the body is subject to the brain. How could it be otherwise? The physicochemical mechanisms that are at the base of man's structure and functions, are essentially the same as those of the other mammals. His body obeys the same laws. His old age is characterized by the same accumulation of toxins and the same slow invasion of the organs by the conjunctive cells, those robust, prolific plebeians which, step by step, choke the noble cells which at length wear out. They are victims of the sacrifice they made to the community by giving up their independence and by taking on a limited role, a particular function, which contributes to the prosperity of the whole society to the detriment of their own powers of resistance.

The human brain embodies all the hopes of the new race, but the cells that compose it are similar to those of the most primitive beings and are nourished like the others. Their functions are regulated by the chemical products secreted by the endocrine glands, and an atrophy or suppression of the thyroid gland can annihilate all the marvelous properties of the brain without any apparent change in the cells. Thought becomes impossible, but we find no difference between the gray cells of the cretin and those of a normal man. I cannot give you other examples for lack of time, but you must remember that the normal equilibrium of man is entirely dependent on the multiple glands of internal secretion: thyroid, parathyroid, suprarenal, pituitary, interstitial, etc. Even character depends on them. A surgical operation can transform a belligerent, courageous man into a poor, feeble, cowardly being whose muscles become atrophied and whose will disappears. The quality of our thought is affected by our internal secretions and uncultivated beings are entirely subject to them. We therefore depend, like the animals, on a complex chemistry, and our relationship, to them is evident.

But the brain also transmits orders which the body obeys and which are not the consequence of internal secretions or of cell lesions. These are precisely the orders which contradict purely animal instincts, such as the instincts of self-preservation and reproduction. The body often revolts against these orders for they impose sacrifice, the suppression of appetites and passions, and the contempt of suffering and death. The foundation of these commands are moral and spiritual ideas—the sentiment of duty Their origin is not physiological, and they seem to struggle perpetually against the remains of the animal in us. This is the specifically human conflict which proves that evolution continues and that man has the choice of separating himself from the animal by an effort of will.

Man—I speak of the evolved man who is as rare as the transitional forms in natural evolution—is therefore *a battlefield,* and the fight is waged between the carnal body and the spirit. But this fight has also been willed. It is necessary so that evolution can continue in the realm of spirit and may participate and collaborate individually with evolution by choosing the path he wants to follow. This choice imposes free will and free will, the supreme liberty, is the prerogative of man and of man alone.

There had to be a certain criterion in the uninterrupted line of beings so that nature could direct herself and make the right choice among the innumerable trials. This criterion is liberty. When we look back as far as the most inferior organisms, we see that each successive class corresponds to a greater liberty: the multicellular being is more independent than the protozoan, the fish more than the mollusk, the reptile more than the fish, the bird more than the reptile, and the mammal more than the bird. There remained a last liberty which could only be attributed to the being who was already the most free—the one who by his morphological structure could utilize it in the direction of progressive evolution. From the moment man acquired a conscience he was definitely separated from the animals. Even through his physiological properties, the shape of his organs, and his internal mechanisms are inherited from the animals, even though unquestionable traces of the gills of his aquatic ancestors are found in the human embryo of a few weeks, it is vain to seek in any animal, including the ones most resembling man like the anthropoid monkeys and the chimpanzees, something which foreshadows conscience.

I mentioned above that the hypothesis of evolution did not seem to be incompatible with the Holy Scriptures and that no real conflict existed between science and religion. My reason for thinking this is that in the first chapter of Genesis—verses 26, 27, 28,—we read:

26. And God said "Let us make man in our image, after our likeness; and let him have dominion over the fish of the sea, and over the birds of the air, and over the cattle, and over all the earth, and over every creeping thing that creepeth upon the earth".

27. So God created man... male and female created he them.

28. And God blessed them, and God said unto them, "Be fruitful and multiply, and replenish the earth and subdue it..."

31. ... And there was evening and there was morning ,a sixth day.

But in the second chapter, verse 7, we read that after having rested on the seventh day—"... the Lord God formed man of the dust of the ground, and breathed into his nostrils the breath of life; and man became a living soul."

Later He created the Garden of Eden (verse 8) and in the middle of it He put the tree of Life and the tree of Knowledge of good and evil (verse 9). Later He forbade man to eat of that fruit (verse 17) under threat of death. Later still (verse 22) He put Adam to sleep and created the first woman from one of his ribs.

The human species, gifted with a conscience, free to choose between good and evil, free to regress towards the animal or to progress further, descends from this second couple, animated by the divine breath, and not from the first who are never again mentioned. The Holy Scriptures must, I think, be thus interpreted. The man they speak of was truly created the moment the human soul was breathed into him; the moment when conscience was awakened in him; the moment he had the choice of deciding his fate himself. The man of flesh, muscles, bones, blood, and nerves, as yet without a conscience, is still only an animal. The man who possesses human dignity, who is free to do good or evil, who is the final goal of all evolution, and who, henceforth, by an act of free volition and an everrenewed effort, must participate in liberating himself definitively one day from the endocrinian slavery; that man is the one God willed, the man of the Scriptures. I am well aware that the orthodox interpretation is very different.

We must not seek the chasm that separates man from the animals in his anatomical structure. It does not exist any more than between the different species of mammals. This is the error made by many scientists, philosophers, and theologians. It led the latter to challenge evolution which nevertheless bears witness by its continuity and grandeur to the divine omnipotence of the Creator. We cannot deny that there has been evolution, even if the mechanisms escape us: all paleontology since Cuvier would have to be destroyed and that is a superhuman task. Every passing year brings hundreds of new proofs and to deny this stubbornly would be to render a bad service to religion, for it is impossible to fight facts. Moreover, why persist? Evolution is in itself a confounding awe-inspiring miracle, if we will only consider it, both in its broad lines and its details, as the process which accomplished the miracle of miracles—the birth of conscience.

Three panels of a triptych—three phases preceded by another different new law for each phase.

Thus, if we adopt this new interpretation, evolution resulted in the human form, but the true man, the free man, was only created when the notion of good and evil (sin) were born in him.

It is the myth of the Garden of Eden, of the tree, and of the knowledge of good and evil. Until he ate of the forbidden fruit, man, like the animals, could not sin for he did not know that he sinned. By forbidding him, God taught him that he was free to sin. But neither could he have progressed for henceforth progress imposes an act of free volition; therefore the possibility of disobeying.

Of all the animals, without excepting the first couple of human form, Man was the only one who was free, the only one subjected to temptation, the only one who was warned of the consequences of his act. It is impossible to speak more clearly in such a symbolic and sometimes cryptic text as the Bible. The birth of man truly dates from the birth of the consciousness of good and evil and only after the original sin do the Holy Scriptures begin.

Therefore the Church is right in refusing to admit the animal origin of man when considering the human soul. But it is wrong if it considers only the human form.

Let us now look at the consequences of this hypothesis. First of all, it enables one to understand the reason of evolution and gives man the place he deserves to hold in it. It does not give it to actual man, as he now is, but to the ideal man, possessor of the divine spark, the man who contrasts with the animal from whom he will increasingly separate himself, by his individual effort, by his highest aspirations. This hypothesis is not in contradiction with any scientifically observed facts whereas the finalist theories proposed up till now generally do not take them into account. I mean by this that the physicochemical laws of the universe, considered today as being essentially based on the role of chance, are respected. All our laws are of a statistical nature. They express the results of an immense number of elementary particles which only obey the laws of chance, and it is precisely from their great number that the laws of chance derive their regularity.

We cannot neglect these laws which are human and express the harmony of nature for the human brain. We do not have the right to decide that on an average they no longer apply to man himself or to evolution. We are not authorized to affirm without proof that they govern only the inorganic world. The chemistry of the digestion, of the renal and hepatic secretions, is identical to experimental chemistry. If there is a difference, as we know there is, between a living organism and a dead organism, it resides in a specific property of the living tissues; a property which orients the reactions produced in it in a determined direction no longer governed by chance. Likewise, an engine will produce disasters when going at full speed on a railroad track without an engineer, whereas this same engine, when driven by a man, will transport travelers and merchandise and will serve the economy of the country.

Our hypothesis therefore consists in introducing a directive will whose ultimate aim, ever since unformed nebulae occupied space, was the appearance of an immaterial conscience, capable of evolving towards a perfect spirituality and of liberating itself from the dictatorship of a material support, which is only its temporary condition.

Only man possessed the necessary qualities. Thanks to articulate speech he introduced a new process of evolution, tradition, which from then on played a primary part in his development. Thanks to tradition the acquisitions of intelligence are no longer lost. Moral and intellectual progress are assured, the spiritual patrimony of man can be indefinitely and rapidly enriched from generation to generation. On the other hand, the progress of animals, who are deprived of this mechanism and reduced to transmitting only hereditary characters to their descendants, is infinitely slow and concerns only morphological and psychological transformations. The transmission of acquired characteristics is still debated.

The most important consequence derived from this theory is that it immediately provides an absolute criterion of good and evil. Indeed, as the will of God is the development of spirit by means of the human conscience and as the mechanism employed is evolution, which must continue, everything that opposes this evolution and tends to make it regress, everything, in a word, which tends to make man regress towards the animal is contrary to the will of the Creator and represents evil.

On the contrary, everything which helps evolution, everything which tends to make it progress, everything which endeavors to separate man from the beast is in conformity with the Supreme Will: it is good.

All the fundamental moral rules, universally shared by all civilizations,

which have existed in writing for the past six thousand years, and have been followed for a much longer time, are the immediate result of this definition. The explanation of less clear and more subtle orders can also be derived from it. For instance, chastity—imposed but not ordered for some individuals—whereas procreation is commanded for others. The great prophets, the mystics, have always been chaste. Catholic priests take a vow of celibacy, and virginity possesses a special and strange value. How do we reconcile this with the brief and non-ambiguous commandment: "Be fruitful and multiply?"

In the light of our hypothesis this last commandment is addressed to the still non-evolved mass whose only role is to maintain the species, whereas chastity is imposed on evolved beings capable of making the species progress in the moral and spiritual realm. This is a higher task reserved for a small number of select individuals who are so rare that only oral tradition has preserved the commandment addressed to this infinitesimal minority. But the prestige of chastity remains: it alone exerts absolute authority over souls because he who practices it has severed all his ties with carnal nature.

In the moral and spiritual order in which evolution is from now on engaged, statistical laws are no longer all-powerful: the individual plays a role of prime importance. Every man is responsible for his own fate and must work not only to assure the forward march of evolution but to assure his own immortality. That is why he alone amongst all living beings is free. He can choose between good and evil, and his future will depend on his choice.

At every moment of his life he is confronted with the possibility of obeying, either the physicochemical solicitations to which all animals are subject, or the clear but often cruel commands of his conscience. He walks on a road with many divergent paths but the one he must follow if he wishes to save his soul and remain a man is clearly marked, though often arduous. That is why he hesitates and gives a thousand excuses, which seem valid to him, when he takes the wrong road. When he yields to his appetites he attempts to justify himself by saying: "I only obey nature, it cannot be evil for nature is divine." *But man must no longer obey nature whose orders apply only to animals.* By obeying nature he shows that he was not worthy of harboring human conscience and of contributing to the eternal plan. He falls, he rejoins the brute, he eliminates himself from the divine plan.

General progress depends on individuals. In like manner animal evolution only progressed through rare transitional forms. They were true monstrosities when they first appeared, but their better adaptation to external conditions, their success in the vital trial, proved their superiority which contained the promise of the coming superiority and was therefore worthy of being conserved. Progress never emerges from the mass whose role consists in providing the human material which, by an unknown mechanism, will from time to time produce the men capable of making their less evolved fellow beings progress. Religions have always increased their number. Materialism has the effect of decreasing it. Worldliness has never produced sisters of charity.

None of us is indispensable, but none of us is useless. As I have already stated, the importance of our role depends on ourselves. Our duty is to contribute to evolution. We can collaborate in two ways, following our aptitudes, according to whether we are already more or less evolved. The first way consists simply in procreating. The species must not perish: Be fruitful and multiply is the commandment given by God in the first chapter of Genesis to the first human couple—male and female. The second way consists in working toward the true evolution of man by improving ourselves spiritually and morally, by example, and by teaching human dignity. It is the command given by God to the second couple, Adam and Eve, invested with the human soul. "Do not sin" and teach your descendants the horror of sin, the horror of regression toward the beast.

Thus in evolved beings the sentiments and desires that result from the activity of internal secretions come into violent collision with others of unknown origin and which are shrouded in mystery for unbelievers. The consciousness of human dignity, as well as daily tragedy, are born from the knowledge of this conflict, from the liberty to choose between the two calls, and from the effort made to subject the animal solicitation to the domination of spiritual orders. The man who possesses this sentiment of dignity can be assimilated to the transitional forms of the past. A very long time may be needed for all men to attain this superior stage, hundreds of thousands of centuries. The struggle will be hard for on the one side are all the sensual pleasures of life, all the solicitations of our bodies, and on the other are all the duties, all the renunciations which are compensated only by joys that the majority of men have not yet learned to appreciate.

The proof that human evolution has only just begun is found precisely in our attachment to sensual pleasures which are a reminder of our origin. The proof that something else exists in us is given by the fact that certain beings have revolted against the physicochemical slavery. This will to break the chains felt by no living being up till then, manifestly establishes the reality of the degree of superior liberty which characterizes man and which makes him the master of his spiritual destiny. The human being ceases to obey a rigorous determinism and henceforth has the power to contribute to final evolution. If he does not use this privilege, if he is physiologically incapable of doing so, his part is restricted to prolonging the species as his inferior brothers have done. He is differentiated from them only by his morphological characters, his shape, and has not yet the right to the name of true man. He has only a statistical value. He is not individually an ascending term.

On the contrary, the heroes, the martyrs, the saints, the prophets, and all those who are ready to die for an idea are the only true craftsmen of evolution. They give us at the same time its direction and the proof of its continuation.

Virtue, good, therefore consists in the individual effort. This should console many anxious souls who ask themselves meaningless questions. Which is the right way? Should I listen to this one or to that one? Is the religion of my childhood the real one? Let them be reassured: the truth is in themselves and is manifested by their effort to attain an ideal which is common to all religions; which is above religions. The mystic, Kierkegaard wrote: "If of two men, one prays to the true God without personal sincerity and the other prays to an idol with all the passion of the infinite, it is the first who in reality prays to an idol, whereas the second one in reality prays to God." And the great Catholic writer Miguel de Unamuno, adds this admirable sentence: "To believe in God is to desire His existence and furthermore to act as though He existed."

What matters the idea we have of God if it can awaken in us the desire of goodness, of purity, of sacrifice, and if it gives us the strength to practice virtue? The only thing that matters is the result obtained and the effort made to free oneself from the ancestral shackles. The cultivated man who succeeds in convincing himself of this truth does not need to create an image of God. He must understand that it is a vain attempt which transcends human intelligence. Personally, if I could conceive God, I could not believe in Him. Every conception entails a part of anthropomorphism which restrains and dwarfs the object one tries to visualize. It is not the image we create of God which proves God. It is the effort we make to create this image.

Human progress manifests itself in different forms which we agree to embody in a general term: the civilizations. The theory of evolution, which I have expounded to you in its broad lines, enables us to give two definitions of civilization in its most general sense, which correspond to its two aspects. Indeed, the word "civilization" evidently has two meanings: a static meaning which expresses a *state* defined at a given moment—European civilization in the year 1700 for instance. From the dynamic point of view, it signifies the development of the factors which have led to this state and which will continue their evolution beyond it: European civilization since the year one thousand.

First, the static definition: civilization is the descriptive inventory of all the modifications brought about by the brain alone in the moral, esthetic, and material conditions of the normal life of man.

235

Second, the dynamic definition: civilization is the manifestation of the conflict between the memory of the anterior evolution which persists in man and the spiritual ideas which tend to make him forget it. You can see that the second definition rests entirely on the idea of evolution which I have just propounded. It is based on a purely moral point of view and enables one to judge the true value of a civilization. For every civilization which tends only to exalt the passions, to encourage gross appetites, to increase the comfort of individuals to the detriment of their spirit, or limit their individual liberties, the primary tool of progress, every civilization which imposes from childhood ideas different from those that develop man's conscience and prepare him to play his role in the evolution of human spirit is—evil.

Intelligence does not develop or spread. The sages of antiquity, the Eleatic philosophers, were as intelligent as we are if not more so. Intelligence deprived of the support of morality leads to the most dangerous excesses, to cataclysms. Moral ideas, on the contrary, can develop themselves and spread, and that is what every true civilization should seek. It is in this direction that humanity should work, for it is the direction of evolution.

But how can this be accomplished? What technique can we resort to? Personally, I can see no hope outside of religion. If our ideal is right, the development of moral ideas, the development of conscience, represents the goal of evolution continued by man. At the present time only a small number of people have attained the stage where spirituality conquers materialism. The role of civilization is to increase this number, but I do not yet know any country on earth where this is the dominating preoccupation. There have been men who have consecrated themselves to this task for thousands of years. Basing themselves on old traditions which apparently developed simultaneously in the four corners of the globe, these men, white or yellow, spread their doctrines which were diversified in form but identical in substance. They thus acquired a wide experience and obtained astonishing results. If they sometimes erred, it does not become others to judge them severely. They will not repeat the same errors in the future. And have they not compensated, for them by numerous sacrifices?

In conclusion, let us remember a phrase written by Renan in Rome: "Never have I better discerned the universality of the eternal law of human nature which modern philosophy has taken too little into consideration: humanity is religious."

And it is truly this tendency which created the religions. They were and are only the concretion of a confused but powerful aspiration which attempted to codify and explain the mysterious commands of conscience. They are only the form given by human intelligence to the distant call of destiny. They condense all the wisdom of the world and are merged in the history of humanity.

It is the religions which have inspired the greatest works of genius. If they occasionally had recourse to myths, to images, let us not forget that they addressed themselves to the mass and that one must speak to the mass as to a child. What matters the truth of the fable if the child is sufficiently impressed to conform to the good? What counts is to extract from man, from those who are incapable of doing it themselves, the spiritual sap which unquestionably exists in all of them, for they have a common origin, first so as to give them the means of being happy on earth and then to prolong evolution by the purification of the spirit.

I have confidence in the future of spirit, in the grandeur and nobility of the part that man is free to play. The struggle for existence and for evolution, of which he is the crowning point, continues, and the fight has lost nothing of its violence by being transferred from the material realm to the spiritual realm. The dignity of the individual must emerge from the effort he makes to break loose from the yoke of the flesh and obey the inner voices.

EVOLUTION AND RELIGION 1944

Just as a traveler, at the fall of day, rests when he reaches the top of a hill and contemplates the distance covered since morning, so every thinking man reaches a period of his life when the details of daily existence lose their importance. He wants to understand the meaning of events and establish his identity as a thinking being in the immense flood of humanity. He is assailed by unaccustomed questions. He becomes conscious of the links that unite him to his universe; he no longer considers himself the center of gravity in a restricted world. He aspires to a less superficial knowledge of the cosmos for he realizes his interdependence.

Happy is the man who possesses an unshakeable faith, the shield behind whose shelter pure souls can keep the smiling equanimity that disdains all curiosity. But it cannot be contested that the heart of many men is the stage of a conflict between the strictly intellectual activity of the brain, based on the progress of science, and the intuitive, religious self. The greater the sincerity of the man, the more violent is the conflict. Personally, I believe that on the one hand this is the result of misunderstandings and, on the other hand, of the difficulty experienced by the cultivated but unspecialized man in basing his opinion on a real knowledge of scientific facts. Indeed, such a knowledge requires many years of reading and research, and the layman usually obtains his information through articles of vulgarization which were too often written for a purpose that had nothing in common with science.

Some of these writers were doubtless sincere. But when they felt they could give free run to their imagination, they did not possess the necessary elements to base their reasoning on solid foundations and they let themselves be carried away by purely sentimental convictions. A superficial scientific coating often gave a reliable appearance to their passionately propagated atheism and could thus impress and even convince those who, being incapable of going to the source, had given them their confidence. Biological writers, such as Haeckel and Le Dantec, perhaps unconsciously perverted the thoughts of great builders like Lamarck and Darwin and seriously harmed the very idea they wanted to defend— the idea of evolution—by adapting it forcibly to the narrow frame of their partisan convictions.

At a time when the world is shaken by a cataclysm without precedent, the need for a common effort of recovery, based on recognizing moral and spiritual values, has never seemed more urgent. When modern inventions by shrinking the planet have united all civilized people against the threat, it seems particularly opportune to seek to conciliate our conceptual image of the universe with the clear, or confused, aspirations of the human spirit, our intellectual activity with moral effort, our science with religion.

From a purely rational point of view we must take both sides into account. They are realities which are questioned today only by a small number of sectarians— religious sectarians who see a danger in the products of intelligence and refuse to admit the possibility of an intellectual and spiritual harmony, and atheistic sectarians who refuse to recognize the reality of experimental facts which cannot be measured or seen under a microscope. They both show a strange kind of daltonism, which could be excused in past centuries, but which today reveals either a lack of imagination or an incomplete knowledge of the physical sciences, of their requirements, and of their obscurities. It is therefore necessary to try and clarify the question for the unbeliever as well as for the believer; for the scientist as well as for the priest.

The most important hypothesis for living beings that has been put forth up till now by human intelligence in the objective realm is evolution. Its interpretation, however, has been the subject of so many sterile fights that it is necessary to make a preliminary restatement of the question based on rigorous definitions.

Today, the Church admits the idea of evolution, but not without restrictions which are badly defined. Science is naturally evolutionist, but the evolutionists are far from being in agreement and have lost their complete confidence of forty years ago.

Is a reconciliation possible? In our opinion it is not only possible, but, rightly or wrongly, it seems to us that evolution must of necessity be incorporated into every integral delineation of man's universe due to the fact that of all phenomena it is the most vast and the most general and it covers all the manifestations and activities of life since its appearance on earth. On the other hand, it also seems to us that no variety of human cerebral activity—rational, intuitive, or any other kind—is independent of evolution. In its entirety it forms a coherent, homogeneous whole, which as I have demonstrated elsewhere[1] is only conceivable if it has been *willed*. The human form is its crowning point. And human ideas—I intentionally do not say thought—are inseparable from the brain. If they were not inseparable evolution would have been useless, and it is inconceivable that this should be the case. Everythings takes place as if ideas and the thought which weaves them were not the consequence of the structure of the brain, but as if the ideas had been willed and had motivated the existence of the brain and therefore of the human form—and therefore of evolution.

The human world is governed by ideas or else by passions and appetites. The appetites are the manifestations of the mechanisms which insure the persistance of the species; their origin is physicochemical. Passions are hypertrophied sentiments often based on appetites that are sometimes pathological. Appetites and passions represent the ancestral heritage

[1] Lecomte du Noüy, *L'Avenir de l'Esprit* (Paris, Gallimard, 1941, New York, Brentano, 1943).

of the animal, heritage which is more or less modified by its passage in the human form. Spiritual, moral, and esthetic ideas, on the contrary, represent a specifically human progress.

To consider moral and spiritual values as a cause is not a paradox even though they were the last to appear. A parallel exists in human psychology. Any inventor who has a goal in view is often obliged to start from a distant point and to study and perfect different instruments, create intermediary parts, and experiment and improve for many years before being able to build the perfect machine he had in mind. Thus the goal can become a cause. This cause is called the final cause and unless we admit a similar finalism in evolution as a whole it becomes incomprehensible.

In his book *The Causes of Evolution* the famous and convinced evolutionist, the chemist J. B. S. Haldane, writes that:

After taking some hundreds of millions of years to attain a primitive type, the Ammonites suddenly took on new characteristics during a lapse of a hundred million years and then, in spite of different attempts at a re-birth, the last Ammonite died. This process was not peculiar to the Ammonites. It seems to have occurred also in the Graptolites, the Foraminifera and other groups. Similar cases can be found in the Gryphea or the Titanotheria, which no theory of evolution can explain. An explanation of evolution should be found outside of the concept of continuity. The phenomena of abrupt advent is most evident amongst the plants. On the other hand, we have the case of the *Cepea* genera which despite a numerous and polymorphic population has shown no apparent alteration for 250,000 years. During more than 400,000,000 years the mollusks belonging to the species *Lingula* and *Patilla* have shown no variation.

The majority of evolutive movements are degenerative. Progressive cases are exceptional. Characters appear suddenly that have no meaning in the atavistic series. Evolution in no way shows a general tendency towards progress... The only thing that could be accomplished by slow changes would be the accumulation of neutral characteristics without value for survival. Only important and sudden mutations can furnish the material which can be utilized by selection.

Another critic who writes on the same subject states: "We are obliged to acknowledge that an evolution which proceeds in such an uncertain manner sometimes towards a greater complexity, sometimes in regression towards the primitive forms of extinction, is very different from the

242

evolution popularized by Darwin in his theory of natural evolution. Direction, persistence, order, universality, all these are missing. The only epithet which applies is change. The idea of evolution has the value of a hypothesis when it is not upheld by facts; similarly it was believed for a long time that the earth was flat."

These lines are overwhelming. Scientists lauded the theories of evolution to the skies, as long as they believed it capable of doing away forever with the necessity of an external intervention even in the guise of a hypothesis. Three quarters of a century later they are obliged to acknowledge a complete failure. Bitterness is apparent in every one of their sentences. We can feel their deception which is predominantly antiscientific. They even deny evolution and blind themselves to the fact that on the whole, in spite of everything, there has been progress from the original cell to man and that man appeared at the top of the ladder. They did not understand the mechanism and could not or did not wish to dissociate the phenomena of transformation and adaptation from evolution itself, because they refused to accept a finality. They are thrown back on the old idea of creation, of absolute beginnings, which they cannot admit and prefer to break their toy rather than to learn how to use it. They betray their scientific conscience so as to remain faithful to their negative faith but are forced to admit its sterility.

Many of the obscurities they complain of pitifully no longer exist when evolution is considered in the light of the telefinalist hypothesis as we expounded it in *L'Avenir de l'Esprit*. But all the mysteries of evolution are far from being solved, and we have no illusions on that score. Physicochemical actions cannot by themselves explain all the mechanisms which bring about the actions we perceive, and the origin of the "points of departure" raises insuperable difficulties at the present time. Let us take a single striking example. It is possible to conceive that an organ like the eye can be perfected after it has been used to see with, but we have not the slightest explanation of how it could develop from nothing. A complex optical center has to be linked with the nervous system before it can function. How can we admit that a mutation due to chance and to natural selection brought about this anatomical and functional combination, which is prodigious even in the most primitive beings, before this organ conferred on those who possessed it a superiority: namely, before it could enable them to see? Here as in many other cases we must acknowledge that we are totally ignorant of most mechanisms of evolution. But this does not prevent us from seeking the unity and harmony in the integral phenomenon by placing ourselves on the scale of man and by taking into account at the same time his rational acquisitions and his deep aspirations.

Some eminent and absolutely sincere scientists who have produced important work suffer from a true allergy to the supernatural: to everything which does not fit into the narrow framework of their scientific experience. I respect their conviction and admire their faith in an all-powerful chance which enables them to consider their own intelligence as its achievement. For, if we refuse to admit a kind of dualism, even though different from the rather childish one of the past centuries, if we espouse the old materialistic thesis, and if we only recognize chance as the unique ultimate cause, then we must necessarily admit that we have chosen this solution by chance and that, consequently, there is one chance out of two that we have made a mistake.

On the other hand, what is the point of view of the creators of the concept of evolution and of broad-minded scientists? In the third chapter of his *Philosophy of Zoology* Lamarck writes: "No doubt nothing exists but by the will of the sublime Creator of all things. But can we lay down rules for the execution of His will and determine the methods He followed? Could not His infinite power create an *order of things* which successively gave existence to all that exists and which is unknown to us?"

Darwin writes: "Authors of the highest eminence seem to be fully satisfied with the view that each species has been independently created. To my mind it accords better with what we know of the laws impressed on matter by the Creator, that the production and extinction of the past and present inhabitants of the world should have been due to secondary causes like those determining the birth and death of the individual. When I view all beings not as special creations, but as the lineal descendants of some few beings which lived long before the first bed of the Silurian system was deposited, they seem to me to become ennobled." [1]

Further on, after having enumerated the laws which produced the different forms of plants and animals he adds: "There is grandeur in this view of life with its several powers, having been originally breathed by the Creator into a few forms or into one [2]."

---

[1] *The origin of Species*, p. 448 London (John Murray, 1859).
[2] *Ibid.*, p. 490.

These texts are evidently never cited by the materialist "exploiters" of evolution.

So much for the creators of evolutionism. As regards the attitude of the greatest scientists concerning God I will cite only the names of a few who were convinced and practicing Christians; Newton, Faraday, Maxwell, Lord Rayleigh, and Lord Kelvin who wrote: "If you think strongly enough you will be forced by science to a belief in God."

A majority of the great scientists in France were believers; Lavoisier, Ampère, Pasteur, and many others. Henri Poincaré, one of the greatest mathematicians of all times wrote: "People ask the gods to prove their existence by miracles, but the eternal wonder is that miracles do not occur all the time. That is why the world is divine, that is why it is harmonious. If it were ruled by whim, what proof would we have that it was not ruled by chance?"

In more recent times a group of American scientists including two Nobel Prize winners, R. A. Millikan and Arthur H. Compton, published a manifesto which reminds one somewhat of Darwin's text: "It is a sublime conception of God which is furnished by science and one wholly consonant with the highest ideals of religion, when it represents Him as revealed through countless ages in the development of the earth as an abode for man and in the age-long inbreathing of life into its constituent matter, culminating in man, with his spiritual nature and all his godlike powers."

Finally, for the first time in the history of science five books frankly finalistic in their orientation were published in France, during the war, in the one month of October 1941: *Invention et Finalism en Biologie* by Professor Cuéno (Nancy), *Message Social du Savant* by Professor Rémy Colin (Nancy), *Anatomie Philosophique* by Professor Rouvoir (Paris), *L'Oeuf et son Dynamism Organisateur* by Professor Dulcq (Brussels) and my own *L'Avenir de l'Esprit*. Needless to say, none of the authors had consulted together beforehand, and this affluence of works represented a remarkable convergence of ideas.

The preceding lines give rise to a curious impression. We perceive a kind of anxiety, of confusion, in the camp of the old school materialists (Haldane and others) who had greeted with enthusiasm the theories of evolution in the nineteenth century, and which leads them to doubt the very idea of evolution. On the contrary, in the camp of the scientists who, though sometimes agnostic, were above all conscientious and did not allow their opinions to influence the results of their scientific reasoning, we find that thorough study of life and evolution leads them to the necessity of a finalism, of God. Lord Kelvin's saying thus receives a notable confirmation.

What are the insuperable difficulties which drove the monist evolutionists (i.e., atheists) to the sort of despair that pierces through their writings? They are of several kinds.

First, a fundamental contradiction between the laws of the inorganic, nonliving world and the living world. The inorganic world is dominated by the second principle of thermodynamics (Carnot-Clausius principle) which imposes a one-way direction to the flow of time (irreversibility) and an evolution of phenomena in the direction of the degradation of energy, of a decrease of dissymmetries, towards an ever-increasing perfect disorder. By perfect disorder we mean a state characterized by a complete isotropy in all realms, the absence of different levels of energy, the potential creators of work. Pushed to the extreme, this concept results in the death of the world by universal cold (no more differences in temperature), by the absence of all movement, complete obscurity, and silence. This is a purely conceptual extrapolation.

But in the evolution of living beings we perceive on the contrary, a progression towards even greater dissymmetries constantly superimposed and combined with one another and generating new properties for over a thousand million years. Recent findings put the age of the earth itself at only two thousand million years.

The materialists counter this argument by saying that it is not at all certain that the second principle does not apply to the biological realm and that life as a whole may only represent a very rare species of "fluctation", but that everything will balance some day and that globally the

Carnot principle applies statistically. To which we will in turn reply that this fluctuation represents the most important event of the world as far as we are concerned, and that it is rather audacious to take advantage of the brain which is directly derived from it to conclude that it is statistically negligible. For, fundamentally, our whole universe as we conceive it exists only in our brains. We ourselves have established the laws relating to ourselves, and we are again reminded of Whitehead's ironical phrase: "... Scientists animated by the purpose of proving that they are purposeless, constitute an interesting subject for study."

Furthermore, even studying current biological problems we constantly find the proof that the laws of inert matter and the second principle do not apply as long as the organ or the organism is alive. As soon as it is dead all our physicochemical laws recover their validity and regulate the equilibria and the exchanges quantitatively [1].

[1] Lecomte du Noüy, *The Road to Reason* (New York, Longmans Green & Co., 1948) where all the questions relating to the significance of science, to the criticism of the methods employed in scientific reasoning, and to the value of the theories are studied in detail and, in particular, the ideas summarized in the four preceding paragraphs.

Some scientists, preoccupied by this question, even pretended that though there had been evolution, there had not been progression and that an amoeba was as complex as a man. If they wished to give a proof of humility they have my respect, but if they consider it a scientific argument then I think we are entitled to smile.

The other difficulties deal with the very mechanism of evolution. "Nowhere is there a general tendency towards progress. The majority of evolutive movements are degenerative. The progressive cases are exceptional," says Haldane. If those are the only obscure points, it seems to me that they are easily answered. We need only observe that they are due to the fact that true evolution is confused with the mechanisms of evolution; i.e., sudden mutations, adaptation, and natural selection.

Let us take the first comment—"Nowhere is there a general tendency towards progress." Does he mean by this that he agrees with certain geneticists and that he perceives no progress between the amoeba and man? I doubt it. I rather think that he sees no progress outside the appearance of man which he considers exceptional. But Evolution, and I here use a capital E, precisely occurred and could only occur in a unique line. All the other lines, those that have persisted until today as well as those that have become extinct in the course of millenniums, only represent unsuccessful trials which continued to adapt themselves but without participating in true evolution. Adaptation is multiple, evolution is one.

The transformations of species are due to the search for an equilibrium between the organism and the surrounding medium. When this equilibrium is attained, adaptation is perfect and the phenomenon stops. The sand worms of the Cambrian or pre-Cambrian period were so marvelously adapted more than 600 million years ago that they have hardly changed, and their descendants differ only slightly from their ancestors. It is not therefore the best adapted who evolve; but, on the contrary, the being who is less well adapted than the others and who possesses a kind of instability which enables him to transform himself still further. I repeat that only one line evolved from instability to instability to finally arrive at man who is perhaps the least well adapted of all living beings. He descends in a straight line from forms which were less perfectly adapted and, as a result, continued to transform themselves. The "persistence of the most apt" imagined by Darwin is therefore not a factor of evolution but, on the contrary, a factor of stagnation; of fixation in the existing conditions of the surrounding medium. All the actual fauna of the world, outside of man, often represent the master-pieces of adaptation but are only the "leftovers" of evolution.

This explains the monstrous shapes and the appendages that became a hindrance as a result of their exaggerated development (antlers of some cervidae). When certain cells are not prevented from proliferating by a regulating organ, they continue to obey mechanically, intelligently so to speak, the laws that are unconcerned with evolution. They are forgotten forms. They will eventually disappear when adaptation can no longer counterbalance the hypertrophy which results from a needless or harmful transformation. This also explains the existence of inimical species, some insects, parasites and microbes. The mechanisms for the transformations that are necessary for evolution work in all directions and often seem to be opposed to progress. In spite of these obstacles, evolution slowly but surely makes its choice and abandons the materials it has used as if disdainful of the preceding forms which have been surpassed. The latter, carried away by their impetus, obey the unbreakable laws of nature just as a car when deprived of its driver pursues its path until it is brutally stopped by a tree or a ditch.

The innumerable extinct branches revealed to us by paleontology are the consequence of the blind efforts of the mechanisms of evolution. They were eliminated at different periods. However, some of them were able to persist by continuing to transform themselves, but without hope of ever rejoining the evolving line; they are the modern fauna. Others persisted without going through transformations because of their acciden-tal isolation in conditions which realized a perfect adaptive equilibrium, like the *Sphenodon Punctata* or *Hatteria*, the only representative of a fifth order of the reptile class, which disappeared during the Jurassic period nearly 150 million years ago but still lives in the rocky islands off the coast of New Zealand. Still others, like the Cetacious, persisted by regressing to the marine medium because adaptation is not itself evolutive.

We can conceive a perfect adaptation brought about by physico-chemical and biological actions resulting from the combined play of mutations, natural selection, and other mechanisms. In that case the transformations stop; the form is fixed. The criterion of adaptation is usefulness; its aim is equilibrium. But a perfect evolution is inconceivable. It is a phenomenon which has no reason to stop for it does not depend solely on external conditions but tends indefinitely towards a distant goal. If we admit that this goal was the spirit, then all the intermediary forms were but trials and the criterion is no longer usefulness, but *liberty*. Independence increases progressively from the protozoa to the Coelenterata and the mollusks; from the mollusks to the fish; from these to the reptiles and then the mammals. It increases first by mobility, then by constant temperature and finally the last-comer, man, wins the supreme liberty, the liberty of conscience. He escapes the endocrinian slavery, all powerful up till then, or rather, he is free to choose between submitting to the ancestral yoke which eliminates him from future evolution, and liberating himself from all which binds him to anterior evolution. The divine spark he harbors within him enables him to dig an impassable trench that separates him from the brute, but he himself must shovel the earth if he wishes to adequately play his human role and continue to evolve further. He is responsible for his fate and for the fate of humanity. Darwin's struggle for life is transferred in conscious man to the moral and spiritual plane and, without losing any of its violence, becomes a conflict which is specifically human; the struggle between the spirit and the flesh from which human dignity will emerge.

The task of man is heavy, but he knows he can attain his goal for he has a perfect model before his eyes which proves that this ideal is also a reality; the dazzling figure of Christ. Henceforth, man's role is clear: evolution, willed by God so that spirit can be born, must continue through the only being whose ascending line has never ceased to evolve. Good, therefore, consists in working for ascending evolution by combatting the instincts inherited from the animal and Evil in regressing towards the beast and submitting to his instincts. Thus, he will collaborate in the eternal work by preparing the reign of spirit.

We cannot hope to expose in a few pages, the arguments in favor of the hypothesis that we have named "telefinalism" in order to differentiate it from the short-term, restricted, finalisms, limited to obtaining adaptive equilibrium. We have attempted in *L'Avenir de l'Esprit* and in another book which will be published under the title of *La Dignité Humaine* to furnish proofs of the plausibility of this theory. But we will deem ourselves satisfied if in the above lines we have been able to throw some light on a few obscure points and convince the sincere man that the study of evolution is in reality the study of divine creation, in the highest sense of the word, and the only ground of reconciliation between science and religion.

EXPERIMENT AND KNOWLEDGE 1944

The prejudicial problems of knowledge

For thousands of years man has been faced with the constant and troubling problem of erecting a conceptual model of the universe that can be superimposed on the one we live in. In other words, the construction of a mental image which tends asymptotically to identify itself with what is called "objective reality."

Volumes have been written, ever since Plato, on the existence or non-existence of this reality and on its relation to the subjective image we have of it. A complete agreement does not seem to have been reached. A few brilliant minds even pretend, with an appearance of reason, that we have hardly progressed. However, we must not be pessimistic, and we must recognize that though philosophical problems, such as objectivity, may now seem out of date and without interest, science, which has replaced philosophy in the last three hundred years, has given us a rich harvest of impressive facts. But the most important contribution of science lies not so much in the facts themselves as in their correlation, their logical sequence, namely in the comprehensive whole of scientific laws. This is where the genius of man has revealed itself in all its greatness. Thanks to these laws he has overthrown the barriers imposed by his sensory system, and the structure of his brain and has finally been able to embrace his whole universe from the subatomic elements to the hyper-galactic worlds. From this point of view, progress is undeniable.

The problem of the identity of this image with the reality which has given it birth, through the intermediary of the senses and of the brain cells, still exists. This does not matter if we have succeeded in constructing a model which is sufficiently homogeneous and coherent to enable us to foresee the evolution of events in time and to calculate their amplitude with growing precision. This model, whether true or false, should satisfy us as long as it does not lead to contradictions between the observation and the prediction, between theory and experiment. We intend to show that such contradictions exist, and that in themselves they constitute a new source of knowledge.

The solidity of our model evidently depends on the rigor and generality of the principles, namely of the fundamental laws which govern not only the facts, but also the laws of detail. Every contradiction between these principles and observed facts will raise problems which will be all the more serious in proportion as the rigor of the principles is better established, all the more disturbing in proportion as our thought is increasingly enslaved by the extension of their generality to a whole part of this universe which we seek to unify.

When an abnormal fact is discovered in a series of facts governed till then by a given law, it can be concluded that this new phenomenon in reality belongs to a different series or else that the law must be broadened so as to embody the phenomenon in question. It can also be concluded that if the new fact was not discovered before then, it was due to an imperfect technique, and this frequently leads to important discoveries such as those of the rare gases of the atmosphere. Thus, either by making the particular laws more supple or by extending them or by establishing new laws, the model has been progressively consolidated and is being further consolidated every day as long as the validity and universality of the fundamental principles are not in doubt. Indeed since Einstein and Minkowsky, any physicist can clearly see that our intellectual model applies to a finite universe.

The significance of our concepts has gained in precision by the introduction of the notion of limitation: limitation of space, limitation of speed (c, speed of light), and as a necessary consequence, limitation of time. These limitations have become the envelope of our reality, and no phenomenon can be considered as real if it overflows the boundaries that we have been obliged to assign to our universe so as to codify its contents intelligently or, if it goes beyond the limits imposed on us by our material experience, when scientifically interpreted. To discredit the fundamental principles on which science rests, we need only to observe a phenomenon where quantities very superior to these limited quantities are brought into play. By very superior I do not mean twofold or tenfold nor even a million times greater, but so important that it would be impossible to invoke an error of calculation or of experiment. For example, *in the present state of our science* we cannot conceive a phenomenon which would necessitate admitting that the dimension of the mean ray of the Einsteinian universe is of the order of 10^{50} light years instead of 10^9, or that the total number of corpuscles is of the order of 10^{200} instead of 10^{79} as certain physicists admit (de Sitter). It would require either a complete revision of our ideas or the introduction of new ideas capable of affecting all our concepts.

In other words, we have established a coherent, homogeneous system covering a vast scale of observations. Though each scale has its own set of laws we have succeeded in making these laws overlap one another in most cases, and it is conceivable that we will succeed in all cases. But this immense task of unification has led us to forge limits in space and in time, and though we have liberated ourselves in certain respects, we have also become slaves of these limitations, of certain principles, and certain modes of thought; statistical thought, for example. Hence, our proud structure would be imperiled today by any phenomenon, or series of indisputable phenomena, which greatly exceeded the conceptual or experimental limits, or put in doubt the generality of a single principle, or necessitated a revision of our modes of thought. For, the coherence and homogeneity of the system of knowledge being menaced, we would have to bolster the edifice and this might be impossible as its structure is conditioned by that of our brains. Or else we have to admit the existence of laws foreign to this system, and this would be equivalent to returning to a dualism considered as antiscientific.

Now, it seems as if at least two facts or two groups of facts, really existed which tend to destroy the harmony of our actual picture of the world. One of them is connected with the question of the limitations we spoke of above and puts in doubt the legitimate application of the sole calculus of probability to *all* the problems of the sensory world. The second attacks the universality of the most unshakable principle of science—the Carnot-Clausius principle, which gives a precise meaning to the notion of the flow of time and of irreversibility.

These two facts are linked together by Boltzmann's interpretation of the second principle, which, as we know, links the evolution of entropy to probability.

The first concerns the appearance of life and even the formation of the first protein molecules which serve as its support.

The second concerns the evolution of living forms which results in the formation of the human brain.

The first problem can be explained briefly in the following manner: The statistical laws and the calculus of probabilities are at the base of all our scientific laws. There are no impossible phenomena, but only highly improbable ones. It is possible to calculate the probability of the appearance of any phenomenon if we possess the necessary fundamental elements. Furthermore it is possible to simplify the problem arbitrarily. This only leads to increasing its probability.

However, we must remember that the duration of the universe is finite according to our present knowledge, and this is where the notion of limit intervenes. The best estimates (Milne, de Sitter, Lemaître, Eddington, etc.,) give for its beginning a figure no higher than 10^{11} years (a hundred thousand million). The number 10^{13} which was proposed no longer seems to agree with the facts. On the other hand, the earth does not seem to have more than 2 or 3×10^9 years of existence (two thousand million years), according to the calculations based on radioactivity.

Finally, it is only for an even shorter time that it has cooled below 100° C. and life seems only to have appeared about twelve hundred million years ago—(1.2 × 10⁹ years).

Consequently, any phenomenon which requires a time greatly superior to these figures in order to appear by the laws of chance, is excluded from the reality represented by our model of the universe. If this phenomenon is well established and indisputable, then there are only two possible hypotheses. The first admits that the rational processes and the mathematical artifices we have imagined to interpret our universe apply only to limited problems, and that phenomena exist which escape our limited laws and are under the jurisdiction of other groups of vaster and as yet unformulated laws. This hypothesis takes away all universality from our modern science and momentarily bars it from certain realms. The second hypothesis admits that the material structure of our brains inexorably imposes certain modes of activity which forbid the rational interpretation of certain perceived facts, i.e., their incorporation in the mechanical model of the universe.

Now the spontaneous appearance, as a result of pure chance, of a highly dissymetrical molecule such as a protein molecule is in contradiction with the laws of chance. By considerably simplifying the problem— which renders the phenomenon more probable— *and if we suppose 500 trillion shakes per second in a material volume equal to that of the terrestrial globe*, we arrive by calculation at the following result [1].

The formation of a molecule of a degree of dissymmetry equal to 0.9 would require on an average the continuation of these shakings during 10^{243} thousand million years. The exponent would become fantastic if we considered the probability of the appearance of 1 kilogram of protein and not merely of one molecule. I remind the reader that the universe has probably existed for 10^{11} years and the earth 2×10^9 years. Exponents superior to 100 correspond to values that have lost all signi-

[1] Lecomte du Noüy, *L'Homme devant la Science* (Paris, Flammarion, 1939), pp. 137 ff. and *The Road to Reason* (New York, Longmans Green, 1948), pp. 123 ff. Charles E. Guye, *L'Evolution Physico-Chimique* (Paris, 1922).

ficance for the human mind. And this does not even refer to life but simply to one of the substances which serve for its support. To give an idea of the immensity of the figures expressed in powers of 10, let me remind the reader that since the birth of the terrestrial globe (two thousand million years) *less* than 10^{17} seconds have elapsed and that the distance from the sun to the earth expressed in thousands of millimeters is 1.5×10^{17}. The objection that the degree of dissymmetry 0.9 for a protein molecule does not rest on a true measurement, and that the first proteins were perhaps much simpler and more symmetrical—therefore more probable—can be countered by the fact that nothing allows us to affirm this. Quite the contrary. Indeed, if our actual proteins have multiple molecular weights of 34,500 (perhaps 17,250), we know that very elementary animals, the mollusks, and among them in particular the gastropods (snails), possess proteins that are much more complex than those of mammals. Their blood pigment (hemocyanin) attains a molecular weight of the order of 6,000,000 which implies a number of atoms (carbon, hydrogen, nitrogen, and oxygen) certainly superior to 375,000 and probably near 500,000. The degree of dissymmetry of such a gigantic molecule cannot be estimated, but a very high value can be attributed to it.

Obviously, I cannot dwell at length on a subject which I examined critically in a work published in Paris in 1939. [1] I will therefore content myself with only pointing out that this prejudicial problem raises serious questions, for it exposes the contradiction between a commonplace, obvious fact and the whole rational system destined to eventually explain it. Not only is the fact not explained but mathematically we are led to consider it as so improbable that it is equivalent to denying its existence.

Let us now go on to the second example which is even more striking than the first—namely the evolution of living forms. We know that the second principle of thermodynamics, or principle of Carnot-Clausius,

Lecomte du Noüy, *L'Homme devant la Science.*

imposes on the universe and on every isolated system an irreversible direction of energetic evolution, towards states that are decreasingly dissymmetrical and decreasingly rich in utilizable energy. Boltzmann showed that these states were also increasingly "probable." The progression of this evolution is expressed by the increase of an important force introduced by Clausius—entropy. This principle is absolutely general and constitutes the backbone of all our science. From a scientific point of view it is impossible to conceive the possibility of a systematic exception.

But the very birth of life introduces new highly dissymmetrical systems on earth which could not be foreseen, and from that epoch on biological evolution has always progressed in the direction of an increase in dissymmetry; namely towards less and less probable systems. No one will deny that the protozoa, although very complex and very dissymmetrical, are infinitely simpler than the vertebrae constituted by an immense number of cells, or that amongst the vertebrates, the homeotherms, the mammals and finally man, do not represent an infinitely greater degree of complexity.

If we consider this second evolution as negligible compared with the first—which energetically might be justifiable—and if we consider it as a single fluctuation, we must nevertheless recognize that this fluctuation has for more than a thousand million years given proof of a remarkable persistence. A fluctuation which maintains itself, repeats itself, and amplifies itself without a break during a length of time equal to half of the age of the earth, can no longer be treated as a fluctuation. And it would be very ungracious on our part to consider it as negligible inasmuch as it is responsible for the fact that we can discuss these questions today, thanks to the existence of our brain.

For us men, biological evolution is infinitely more important than the inorganic evolution conceived by the tool which was slowly elaborated by the first, namely our brains. And only a paradoxical mind, or one that is strangely blind, can delude itself to the point of attributing more reality to the chemical substance of the brain than to the ideas—no matter how imponderable they are—which have allowed it to study this substance and to formulate its laws.

There are thus two facts, amongst a hundred others, all relative to life, which do not enter into our intellectual model of the universe. Our "image" therefore applies only to our inorganic world as it is represented by the brain, but it is incapable, up till now, of including this brain and all the preceding events which have contributed to its creation.

There is therefore no doubt that from the philosophical point of view this established fact is of fundamental importance, for it reveals the existence of a realm of transcendent laws the effects of which we perceive without discerning their cause.

It is interesting to note that when we logically admit the reality of these transcendent laws and consider them in connection with the destiny and responsibility of man, they enable us to catch a glimpse of horizons that are immeasurably more luminous than those given by the assimilation of the human being to a physicochemical system enslaved by its endocrine secretions.

Human "Physiological Time" and "Psychological Time"

Since the earliest ages, man has been preoccupied by the measurement of time. His task was facilitated by the existence of certain sense impressions which repeat themselves periodically, are always identical to themselves, and correspond on an average to the same routine of conscious states. The alternation of day and night, for example, has been employed since the beginning of the history of man to register approximately the same sequence of psychological events: a day and a night became the measurement of a certain interval of consciousness.

This primitive method was perfected in the course of centuries but remained fundamentally the same. Today we refer to the regular movement of the hands of our clocks because we know that this movement is determined by the motion of the earth around the sun. By admitting furthermore, as a result of astronomical experience, that the time intervals represented by a day and a year have a constant relation, we can throw back the regulation of our clocks on the motion of the earth about its axis. If an observer watches a so-called circumpolar star, namely one that remains all day and night above the horizon, he will see that, like the hand of his astronomical clock, it describes equal parts of a circle in equal times measured by his clock. In this manner the hours counted by the astronomical clock, and ultimately by all ordinary watches

265

and clocks regulated by it, correspond to the earth turning through equal angles on its axis. We base our measurement of time on the earth taken as a chronometer.

All goes well up to now, the reasoning follows the experiment and remains homogeneous. But this is no longer the case when we admit that equal rotations correspond to *equal intervals of consciousness*. We fall into pure and arbitrary hypothesis. For as all the clocks are situated on earth and identically regulated, how can we be certain that the earth is a regular timekeeper? If the earth were gradually to turn a little more slowly upon its axis, how should we know that it was losing time and how should we measure the amount? It could be said that we would find that the year contained fewer days, but how could we affirm that it was the day that was growing longer and not the year that was growing shorter? Again it may be objected that we know a great number of astronomical periods relating to the motion of the planets expressed in terms of days, and that we should be able to tell by comparison with these periods. To this we must answer that the relation of these periods expressed in days and in terms of each other now appears invariable. But what would happen if all these relations had changed slightly in the last five or ten thousand years? Which body would we consider as having gained or lost time? Or, what if the ratios of their periods remaining the same, they were all to have lost or gained? How could we assert in such an eventuality that the hour today is the same interval as it was ten thousand or a million years back? Now certain investigations with regard to the frictional action of the tides make it highly probable that the earth is not a perfect timekeeper, nor are we able to postulate the regularity of motion—by which alone we could reach absolute time—of any body in our perceptual experience. The perfect uniform motion escapes us experimentally. It is only reached conceptually, like the movement in a straight line and the geometrical surface, by carrying to the limit the approximate identity and uniformity which we observe in certain movements perceived by our senses.

The human notion of time therefore depends on our sense system

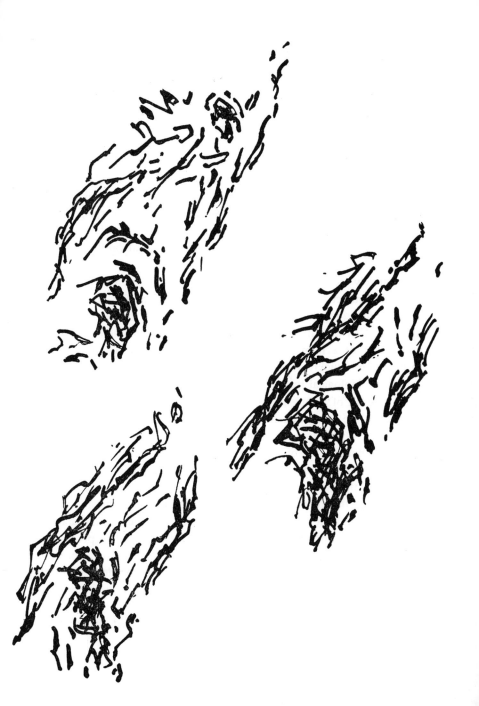

and on our consciousness, namely on our activity as a human being. Now a living being obeys particular laws, and it seems possible to establish a distinction between it and the inorganic world: the world of rocks and minerals and the world of beings who evolve between birth and death according to a hereditary rhythm indefinitely renewed. Consciousness arises out of "nothingness", develops itself, enriches itself, and returns to nothingness. All the reality of man is registered between a cradle and a tomb. But the reality of the human species is spread between infinitely greater limits, as is that of all living species. Is the value of time the same for beings who have an individual beginning and end, following a very short cycle, as for a species that can be practically considered immortal or as for inorganic matter?

Intuitively we realize that the value of time is not the same for an ephemeral insect which lives only for a few days as for man who lives up to eighty or a hundred years. The rhythm of the reactions is not identical. Can we affirm that their value is the same at the beginning and at the end of a human life? Experience teaches us that time "seems" to flow more quickly as we advance in age. Is this an illusion or on the contrary a biological reality? We will try to answer this question.

As a result of a long series of experiments begun during the war of 1914-1918, we succeeded in showing that the rate of the cicatrization of wounds varied as a function of the area of the wound and of the age of the patient. We obtained a simple mathematical formula in which a single coefficient expressed this double relation, and we named this coefficient "the index of cicatrization."

Thanks to this formula it was possible for the first time to calculate in advance the date of complete cicatrization and the successive dimensions of the wound. The principal advantage consisted in possessing a curve which represented a normal evolution of a wound at a maximum velocity. This enabled us to study antiseptics and socalled "cicatrizing agents" in relation to a standard which eliminated any personal and often fanciful appreciation.

During the following years, after we had conceived the possibility

268

of the existence of a "physiological time" different from "physical time" or astronomical time, we tried to eliminate the individual element of the formula; namely the influence of the area of the wound:—a small wound cicatrizes more rapidly than a large one in a man of a given age. This result was obtained by means of a mathematical artifice which simply consisted of multiplying the index of cicatrization by the square root of the area of the wound. We called the new coefficient thus obtained the *Constant of physiological activity of reparation A*. It now depended only on the age of the man (or of the animal) and expressed, as its name indicates, the specific activity corresponding to a given age.

The experimental values of the coefficient A, based on a large number of cases, more than 600, are the following:

Age	10	20	25	30	32	40	50	60 years
A =	0.400	0.260	0.225	0.198	0.188	0.144	0.103	0.08

These figures show that the healing activity of the tissues varies considerably during the course of a life: it is five times greater at the age of 10 than at the age of 60. Schematically a wound which cicatrizes in 20 days in a child of 10, will cicatrize in about 31 days in a man of 20, in 41 days in a man of 30, in 55 days if he is 40, in 78 days if he is 50 and in a 100 days if he is 60. The activity therefore decreases very rapidly. It is probable that under 10 years the speed of cicatrization is much greater: of the order of 12 times that of a man of 60 at the age of 5, but we have no experimental evidence for very young children.

On the other hand, when experimenting on cold-blooded animals, namely animals whose blood maintains itself at the temperature of the surrounding medium, (reptiles and alligators), we were able to show that the rate of cicatrization depended, like all chemical reactions, on the temperature: the higher the temperature, the more rapid is the pheno-menon. Chemical phenomena are therefore at the base of the phenomena of tissue reparation. Later on we will see why we insist on this point. But the important fact is that at the normal temperature of 37° C, the rate of cicatrization is 5 times more rapid at 10 years of age than at 60.

What does this signify exactly? It signifies that *at different ages differ-ent times are needed to accomplish the same work.*

Now, we can measure time not only by a supposedly constant rate of velocity, like that of the rotation of the earth, but by a work performed if we are certain that this task is performed at a constant speed. It would therefore seem that we cannot measure time by basing ourselves on the rate of cicatrization as we have precisely demonstrated that this varies during the course of life. On the other hand, we must remember that this variation is only observed *by comparison with a standard of time borrowed from the inanimate world;* from the movement of the heavenly bodies which seem to evolve in a uniform, arithmetical time. But there is no evident reason for this physical, conceptual time to apply to living organisms which are born, live, and die and are the seat of essentially different phenomena than those of the inorganic world which ignores individual periodicity, adaptation, and phylogenetic evolution. The rhythm of our cellular existence is infinitely more important for us than the eternally indifferent system of the planets and the suns. We only know the universe through the internal image erected in our brains by means of the reactions of our nervous insertions. This is an immaterial image without doubt, but it represents all our reality, spread between birth and death, outside of which we are sure of nothing. So that our time, the individual time of living things which are born and die, is more real, more significant for us than the mathematical time *conceived* by us but foreign to our vital activities. And nothing obliges us to partition our internal life by means of the rigid framework borrowed from an evolution which is not our own. If we choose to interchange our standards and to measure physical time by means of physiological time, we perceive that everything takes place as if physical time flowed much more rapidly at the beginning of life than at the end, logarithmically—like that of radioactive atoms—and no longer arithmetically.

This immediately explains the fact that we brought to the attention of the reader at the beginning of this article; i.e., that time seems to us to flow more rapidly at the end of life than at the beginning. This is not an illusion but a real fact: a sidereal year is shorter for an old man than for a child.

Let us now see if our experiments on cicatrization will enable us to *measure* the shortening of our years.

We pointed out above that the basic phenomena of the process of cicatrization were of a chemical nature. If we could demonstrate that our appreciation of the velocity of the flow of time, which is a general psychological phenomenon, is fundamentally of a chemical nature, namely that it depends on the temperature in a given proportion (coefficient of Van't Hoff), we would be justified in considering that time plays an identical role in these two phenomena and, consequently, in applying to the second the quantitive relation discovered in the first.

The experiment has been made and controlled by several authors: lately by Professor Hoagland in the United States. Space is lacking to describe these experiments, but they clearly put in evidence the fact that our appreciation of the velocity of the flow of time depends, like cicatrization, on the temperature coefficient of Van't Hoff. We thus have the proof that we possess a chemical clock inside us which measures the velocity of one of our most fundamental activities, the reparation of our tissues and determines the rhythm of our psychological activity. We are therefore authorized to measure the one by the other.

Another mathematical proof has been given in the following manner. We know that a psychological idea of the value of time at different ages is given by the following reasoning: for a child of 5, one year represents the fifth part of its total existence and hardly a fourth of its conscious existence. For a man of 50, a year represents only the fiftieth part of his existence. It therefore appears much shorter to him. Now, curiously enough, mathematical curves, (equilateral hyperbola and logarithmic curves) expressing, on the one hand, these observations and, on the other hand, the variations of the constant of physiological activity of reparation A, coincide, for an important part of their length, between the ages of ten and eighty.

We can therefore measure the shortening of our years and the relative value of the time of our clocks at different periods of our life and we see that one hour of existence for a child of 10 is equivalent to 5 hours of life for a man of 60. In other terms, in the course of sixty minutes of time by our clocks, a child has physiologically and psychologically lived as much as a man of 60 in 5 hours.

We can now understand why it is difficult to keep the attention of a child for more than ten minutes: this length of time is equivalent to fifty minutes of the life of a mature man, and all lecturers know that the interest of their audience begins to falter at the end of that time.

We can thus also understand why a child of 13 does not want to play with a child of 10. Those three years of difference do not count for a grown man but correspond in childhood to important differences in the rhythm of all their activities (23 percent in the above example, 75 percent between 5 and 8 years). Perfect understanding is only possible between certain limits that narrow in proportion to our youth, and to realize it completely there must be a "resonance" between the rhythms. When one advances in years the divergences are narrowed, attenuated. Between 27 and 30, the difference is only 4 percent. Between 50 and 60, it is less than one per thousand and therefore completely negligible.

Human beings—especially in childhood and in youth—are therefore isolated like individual bubbles which touch without mutually penetrating each other; only the proximity of age establishes a synchronism between them which abolishes the barriers and brings about a unity resulting from the identity of the appreciation of the value of time. Outside of age, only the intuitive divination of true love can draw human beings closer and enable them to amalgamate.

Parents, teachers, and children live in temporarily different worlds.

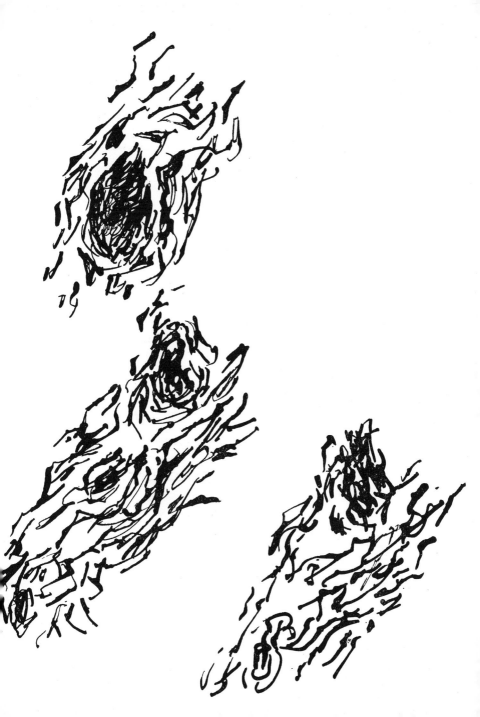

This fundamental fact has been completely neglected up till now, but its consequences are important. The master and the instructor tire the child by demanding a prolonged and useless effort, but they never completely utilize the available resources of a being whose activity is much greater than theirs. A normal child of 12 could accumulate without any fatigue all the knowledge that he generally acquires at the age of 15 or 16. A real understanding of the considerable value of physical time for children would bring about an immense progress in education and in the quality of the individual.

IMPRIMÉ EN FRANCE, FIRMIN-DIDOT, PARIS-MESNIL-IVRY
DÉPOT LÉGAL QUATRIÈME TRIMESTRE 1966 : 2339
NUMÉRO D'ÉDITION 2164
HERMANN, ÉDITEURS DES SCIENCES ET DES ARTS